Rudolf Weinhold

# VIVAT BACCHUS

Rudolf Weinhold

VIVAT
BACCHUS

A History
of the Vine
and
its Wine

Argus Books

Translated from the German by Neil Jones
Edited by Ben Turner
Copyright © 1978 by Edition Leipzig
English edition published by Argus Books,
14 St James Road,
Watford, Hertfordshire, England.

ISBN 0 85242 491 4

Design: Walter Schiller, Altenburg
Cover design, end-paper and drawings:
Angelika Kurth, Leipzig
Production: Druckerei Fortschritt Erfurt

Printed in the German Democratic Republic

*Dust-jacket, front: October.*
*Fresco from the Castello del Buonconsiglio,*
*Trent, about 1400*

# Contents

# Introduction

*1 Vine trained up stake.*
*From: Sebastian Münster,* Cosmographia, *1544.*

Vivat Bacchus is an immensely detailed study of the vine and its wine since the beginning of civilization. Rudolph Weinhold – an appropriate name if ever there was one – follows the path of the vine around the world from Antiquity until modern times. He traces its origins from the wild vine to the cultivated vine, from Babylon through all points of the compass. He traces the development of many of the now almost countless varieties and pays homage to the peasants and workers in the vineyard.

He unfolds the history of vine technology through pruning, training and cultivation of the soil, against a background of enemies from frost to phylloxera, from birds to mildew. No detail is too small for his description.

From the treading of the first grapes to the modern balloon press he helps us to discover all the equipment ever used and the methods of making different wines. He tells us about people whether in myth or legend or fable, about pagan deities and what one might call oeno-hagiography.

The prodigious knowledge that he has gathered together in *Vivat Bacchus*, ranks Rudolph Weinhold as a scholar of the highest eminence. His intense love and enthusiasm for the vine and those who tend it, and for wine and those who make it, is revealed on every page. His book is a poem of praise and thanksgiving of epic proportions and dimensions. For this reason no attempt has been made in the translation or editing to change the flowery lyricism of the original German.

The vast number of illustrations reveal not only every aspect of the cultivation of the vine and the making and maturing of wine throughout its long history, but also a level of research that commands our admiration. If genius be an infinite capacity for taking pains, then Rudolph Weinhold is such a genius of the first growth.

*Vivat Bacchus* is both a joy to read and a joy to look at. No oenophile could possibly turn away uninterested. Indeed, like wine itself, this book will be wanted by the wine lover, to possess, to savour, to enjoy, to contemplate. This is not a book for lending or sharing but for keeping, so that its pleasures may be renewed upon every visit of the Ausonian muse. The chapters are short, no longer than a glassful. But happily the cask is large and its wine will fill many glasses.

BEN TURNER

# Preface

The Hungarian King Matthias Corvinus, who lives on today in the tales and songs of his people, is the subject of a story that illustrates his character. It shows not only the regard in which his subjects held this Renaissance prince, but also the respect he felt for the work of simple men.

The king liked to get away occasionally from being the centre of his luxurious court. Politics could then give way to the Arts. Of the pleasures of the table there was never any lack and when the occasion arose there would be feasting and drinking from morning till night. One day, when this merry company was staying at a hunting castle in the north of the country, not so very far from Tokay, it occurred to the king to take the gentlemen among his companions – already a little the worse for wear from wine – for a walk through the nearby vineyards. The cheerful band was soon out among the wine-growers, watching the hard toil of the bondmen, at first with interest, then with increasing boredom. Matthias appeared not to notice. He began talking with one of the peasants, had the work explained to him, and without more ado grasped the heavy pick and set enthusiastically about breaking up the hard, dry soil. Moreover, he motioned to his companions that they too should lend a hand. His action caused some long faces and even some downright dismay, but no one could get out of it. Soon a remarkable band of vineyard workers in court dress were busy wielding hoes. The peasants, so unexpectedly relieved of their tools, stood by, somewhat at a loss, until soon, however, their natural humour got the better of their nervousness. The sight of their masters doing some honest work was altogether too funny. Their lordships noticed the half concealed laughter, and the heat of the withering scorn added a few more drops to the sweat of unaccustomed toil. But the king seemed oblivious to all this and the withering looks escaped his normally so attentive eye. He swung his pick with an easy rhythm, while the blows of his followers fell ever slower and weaker. Their lordships had no choice but to struggle on amid groans and complaints, until the king decided to call it a day. With trembling, blistered hands they staggered home. The lesson which their king had given them that day is preserved for us in an Hungarian poem:

> "A stubborn thing, your lordships, is the soil,
> And he who must it hoe
> Waters it with the salty drops
> That from his face do flow.
> Raising your glasses, think
> Of this hard toil,
> And find it meet,
> the People's health to drink."

It is not recorded how long the objects of this lesson were remembered. Possibly they faded even quicker than the blisters on their hands. But that does not alter the fact that Matthias gave a very emphatic – and enduring – demonstration of those basic truths which, even today, we all too often forget. They do not apply to wine-growing alone.

But – obedient to the spirit of the poem – wine-growing is our subject. The centre of our attention will be those who tend the vine and those who turn the juice of its grapes into a wine. But producing a splendid drink is not the only value created by their labour. We have to look a great deal wider and embrace everything which directly or indirectly has sprung from their work. Think, for instance, of the wealth of legends and myths and the countless works of art and literature, which have taken as their theme the toil of the wine-grower, and reproduced its fruits in a thousand varied forms. Few people will be aware that science, too, has profited from wine. The man who discovered the secret of fermentation was rewarded with the Nobel Prize, but who can imagine how the cultivation of the vine shaped the lives of those who tended it and spread it abroad; or of those who gathered the knowledge to perfect wine-making; or of those who passed down the memory of these achievements in their legends from generation to generation?

This book is an attempt to filter a few dominant tones from the depth of these echoes. It starts by taking us back to times more remote than the oldest written records. We will follow the vine in its progress over every continent.

We will examine it in the vineyard, and accompany the wine-grower in his work, from hoeing in the early Spring until the vintage in Autumn. And at the end comes the visit to the cellars. Our stocks contain every variety, from every age and from all lands.

But enough of this introduction. It is time to set off into the vineyards. He who has a good bottle should take it with him. A generous drop also aids reflection!

2 *Vines trained on yolks.*
*From a translation of Aesop, Ulm 1476.*

# A Journey through History

 *Myths and Legends*

The ancestry of our cultivated plants, in its essentials, has now been traced. During the last hundred years, botany (especially genetics), as well as archaeology, ethnography and linguistics have made significant contributions to our knowledge. From their mosaic of fragmentary insights emerges an imposing synthesis, giving us an historical picture of how man, from small beginnings, set about assuring himself of his daily bread. Slowly the range of plant foods from which we now live was built up: barley, wheat, rye, millet, rice, maize, oats, olives, figs, dates, apples, pears, plums, cherries, and, last but not least, the grape. Hard-working men of all races and from all parts of the globe, shared the responsibility for these achievements.

Quite frequently, they also preserved vague memories of their creative labour, albeit not in any form accessible to us today. The chronicle of those ancient times conceals more than it reveals, for it transforms history into stories or, rather, into myths, fairy tales and legends. Thus the historical event was detached from its real context and instead brought into association with forces that men thought of as supernatural. According to this way of thinking it was not man with his intelligence, his patience, his untiring industry, who had created the useful plant, but his gods, heroes and saviours who did it for him and before him. Some students of mythology have wanted to see real people behind these beings: people elevated by posterity into immortality in honour and in explanation of their services. But they forget what a complicated process the rearing of a single cultured plant is; how many skills of the most varied kinds had to be gathered and repeatedly tested by hard work.

Such a process is not for one man, one village or one tribe to master. Such prodigious achievements were the work of many generations. Women must have taken a very important part in them. The myths themselves, with the figure of the earth goddess, the protector of the sowing, the multiplier of fertility, the "Great Mother", suggest as much. We meet her under many names: as Ishtar and Astarte with the Babylonians and Phoenicians, as Demeter for the Greeks and Ceres for the Romans. These last two were both credited by the Ancients with having first taught men how to sow corn.

One of these early traditions also links women with the plant which is the subject of our attentions here. The Sumerians, who founded city-states in Mesopotamia over six thousand years ago, acknowledged the goddess Gestin as the protector of the vine. She is probably the descendent of an old, central-Asian, earth goddess. Much later still, around the borders of the Near East, the memory of woman's contribution in the establishment of the vine was very much alive. This much is clear from a text scratched on clay tablets in the mid-second century, found in Ugarit, a famous Phoenician trading city. It tells the story of Pagat, who helped her father Danel, himself a demi-god, in the cultivation of the vine.

In Egypt, on the other hand, as far as we can tell from tradition, the male principle dominated the business from the very beginning. Osiris, who was later to become the god of the dead, reigned during Antiquity, as during the Old Kingdom, as lord of wine. Thousands of years later when the Greeks began filtering into the empire of the Nile they identified him with their Dionysus, not least because this god of wine had also acquired in the course of time a certain authority over the underworld.

The ancestors of the Chinese were thought to have learned the knowledge of wine-growing from an emperor by the name of Yü in about 2,200 B.C. Chroniclers, in fact, are not totally agreed on the matter, other traditions claiming that it was precisely this ruler who acted with terrible vigour to stamp out alcohol. But this account refers to rice wine. When Yü was brought the newly-discovered drink, he apparently dashed the brimming cup to the floor and prophesied that the day would come when it would bring about the fall of a kingdom. Thereupon he expelled the first producers from his country and forbade the further manufacture of the heady brew; as a result of which the Chinese, in part for the edification of posterity, subsequently adopted rice wine as their national drink. But since early times the fall of states has had other causes than fermented rice grains or grapes. In this Emperor Yü was fundamentally mistaken.

The first taste of wine seems also to have been received in other ways. A Persian story recounts an event which apparently took place at the court of King Dshemshid, who is doubtless identical with a popular hero of Iranian mythology.

"The grape, that most delightful of fruits, does not keep long when the cold begins with the changing of the seasons. But many would like to enjoy it in Winter and Spring, too. Thus Dshemshid gave orders that the juice of the grapes be pressed from the skins and seeds, and brought before him each day, that he might, on the touchstone of taste, himself judge the nature and condition of it. He did this until the juice became bitter. Then the king supposed it to be poison, and had the vessel put away and sealed. A beautiful and favoured slave girl was later found to be suffering from headaches so unspeakable that she preferred to die. To this end she chose the well-kept, deadly poison. When she had taken but a little she felt herself cheered and enlivened, the pain eased. She drank more, whereupon she fell asleep, although she had not slept for several days. She slept for a day and a night without pause, and when she awoke was cured. This came to the ears of Dshemshid, whose soul was cheered. He esteemed wine, enjoyed it, and made it the drink of all. And since many who were sick grew well from it, it was given the name royal medicine."

Another, much later, account from the same region reads less lyrically. At that time – the fifth century – Persia was ruled by the line of the Sassanids. One of their administrators, Shemiran of Chorassan, was brought grape pips by an eagle, the emissary of heavenly powers. The seeds took well and bore rich fruit. On the advice of his wise men Shemiran had the juice of these grapes stored in vats. But imagine the confusion of the Court when the juice, after a short while, began to ferment violently. They asked how the juice could be boiling without fire beneath it? But the bubbling lasted only a few days before the liquid began to clear, and stayed clear and red as a ruby.

Of course, no-one actually dared to taste this remarkable liquid. What would happen to them? The noble lords were only too anxious to find out, but none of them had the courage to test it themselves. Thus Shemiran, without more ado, gave orders to test the effect of the drink on a prisoner already condemned to death. He was, after all, used to treating the lives of his subjects a little lightly. The pour soul had to swallow the drink before the eyes of the Court. At the first mouthful he shuddered. But after a short consideration – perhaps he was appreciating the finish – he expressed himself ready for more. To the astonishment of the observers the delinquent showed not the least signs of collapse, but instead became more and more cheerful. He sang, gabbled, tried to dance, and then, to the amazement of all present, asked for another beaker of the sparkling potion. But the end was sudden. With the cup still in his hand the condemned man fell over like a log and slept the deep sleep of all good drinkers, smelling of wine and smiling beatifically. And he had not expired, as his audience discovered after a good deal of shaking and kicking. His drunken snore echoed through the windows of the palace, informing all who could hear him that, for once, the authorities had fundamentally miscalculated.

The next morning, hung-over, but still alive, the prisoner had to submit to an exhaustive inquest about himself. The Court wanted to know everything about this miracle potion, of which the happily resurrected man was already requesting more. The first cup, he explained, had not really tasted particularly good; it had been sour and rather bitter. But nonetheless he was soon

overtaken by the desire for a second cup. This brought joy to his heart. He, who, of all emotions, was best acquainted with fear, and who rated himself but lowly, suddenly saw the whole world differently. The Prince and his Court had seemed less and less awful. Would that such a state had continued for ever! But while carefree joy swelled in his breast, he had been overcome by a great tiredness, and had sunk into deep sleep. But enough of this talking. Another taste, and not too small please, would surely be in place.

Shemiran in considering the fate of this poor soul followed the principle that no criminal should be called on to die twice, and so the discoverer of the intoxicating drink was allowed to go free. The Prince and his Courtiers tried the effect of the noble liquid the very same day. They found it so splendid that they recommended the use of wine and the establishment of wine-making concerns to all the people of the country. It may be that many who received this message had, nevertheless, to stick to more modest drink, not having the resources for the new, superior one.

## 🌿 Dionysus, God of Wine

From the Near East the vine is supposed to have made its way to Hellas. This event is associated with the memorable voyage of Dionysus, who in Antiquity was revered as the protector of the vine, Lord of blissful intoxication, and no less as the incarnation of demonic delirium. Later the Romans named him Bacchus, from his Lydian name *Bakchos*, and doubtless also because they associated their word for the grape – *baca* – with him.

Dionysus, according to a Greek tale, was attacked on the coast of Asia Minor and carried off by sailors who combined trading with piracy. Unaware of whom they had violently assaulted, they forced the boy to serve on the ship. For a time the god did them this service, good-naturedly and even with a little scorn. But then he wrought a miracle that quite dismayed them. On the mast and rigging began to sprout vines, whose grapes instantly ripened and oozed fragrant wine. The rough sailors scrambled greedily for the streaming liquid, and drank themselves into a stupor. And then the god's anger overtook them. With horror the reeling drinkers saw a lion by the god's side, roaring and crouched in readiness to spring. Their only escape was over the side, whereupon they themselves were the victims of another wonder. Engulfed by the waves, they turned into dolphins, and, from then on, were the constant companions of the god on his voyages. Dionysus's ship, overgrown with vines and surrounded by dolphins, remained a favourite motif with Greek vase painters. Their works of art captured a memory that the cultivation of the vine had come to them over the sea, out of the East.

Who was this god to whom such a deed was attributed? We can search the Iliad and the Odyssey for him in vain. For Homer, Dionysus had no rights of residence on Olympus. He seems to have been foreign to the religious beliefs of Homer's heroes. But reports from relatively earlier times reveal that a god of this or a very similar name was worshipped in the Balkans in those regions where the tribes and tribal groups of the Thracians were settled. For them he was one of the foremost deities. His place of worship could be found in lonely mountain regions. Hares, roe-deer, ibex and aurochs, as well as certain trees, the wild vine and ivy, were dedicated to him. As Dionysus Dendrites, protector and multiplier of wild plants and forest creatures, he was also no stranger to the Greeks. They knew that honey, flower oil and wood resin should be dedicated to him. In his honour orgiastic dances took place, where the participants dressed themselves in the skins of wild animals. Memories of the old forest god lived on in later forms of worship. Even when Dionysus's special competence had been restricted to the vine, his statue was still decorated on major holidays with ivy, honeycomb, grapes and chains of dried figs.

When and where wine gained precedence in the cult of Dionysus has not been exactly established. But there is much to suggest that the change was accomplished south of the Balkans. Greek peasants there recognized his competence in the new job. They themselves had contributed to the metamorphosis, attaching to the new figure certain of the Cretan-Aegean cult traditions which they had preserved in their legends. His attribute was, from now on, the cultivated vine plant, and he was accompanied by goats, donkeys, lions and panthers (Ill. 19). Around him swarmed an entourage of satyrs, silens and nymphs (Ill. 8, 13, 14). Thus his tumultuous retinue mixed the ancient and savage with more pastoral and peasant elements.

This Dionysus was a homely god. Countrymen knew that he had no place among the Olympians, and that he shared none of their customs. They loved him because he used to visit them, talk to them, shared their concern for the vineyard – or so their myths recounted. Velázquez left us an incomparably beautiful picture of Dionysus among wine-growers (Ill. 10). It shows the triumph of the god, and at the same time the victory of noble wine.

But in the stories told by the peasants of Ancient Greece, Dionysus did not dwell the year round among mortals. In the winter months, the period when no work is done in the vineyards, he left them. To the underworld, to the dead, said some, drawing on an old tradition by which he died along with the crushed grapes and was resurrected only in Spring, with the fresh sprouting of the vine. A painting from Pompeii plays on this parallel (Ill. 11). Other storytellers pictured him sailing on long voyages to the most distant lands. He was even supposed to have made one such expedition to teach the people of India the cultivation of the vine. The search for the vanished god formed a basic element of the ancient Dionysus cult. It was taken up at first by the peasantry. In November and December after the end of the vintage they celebrated their Dionysia. The procession in which all took part was aimed at the increase of fertility and, for this reason, the symbol of the phallus was also included. It simultaneously expressed the idea of uninhibited merriment that accompanied the celebrations.

It seems that the cult of Dionysus found its way little by little into the official rites of city cults during those centuries in which the Greeks were conquering the lands of the Mediterranean and establishing colonies. In Corinth this happened in 600 B.C. One would not be far out in identifying one of the compelling factors in this process as the growing importance of wine-making and, above all, of the wine trade for wealthy landowners who were influential in

*3 Bacchus. Marginal illustration by Albrecht Dürer for the prayerbook of Emperor Maximilian, 1515.*

the lives of the cities. Small wonder that Diony-sus now became a favourite of theirs, too, his protection valued and his portrait engraved on their coins (Ill. 12).

Under the influence of the cities the celebration of the Dionysia grew to baroque dimensions. The simple celebrations in late Autumn, which were closely connected with the working year of the peasants, were now followed in December and January by the Lenaea. They were an occasion for orgiastic gatherings, although later also for the performance of classical comedies. But the major feasts now became the Anthesteria in February and March. They corresponded to the return of the god with the Spring and the end of the search for him, for which teeming, ecstatic crowds of masked women gathered in the preceding nights. The religious mania which seized these groups included demonic elements from the time of the lord of the forests: any animals they caught they tore to pieces, and devoured raw lumps of the flesh.

The main feast proceeded in four stages. On the first day they opened the pithoi, large storage vessels full of wine, and transferred the contents to more readily transportable amphorae. The second day was for drinking. A general drinking bout drew slaves and even children into the abandoned gaiety. All children of three and over were treated to wine. Perhaps there was some magical association in this, for in the third year of its growth the vine is developed and able to bear fruit. The following night and the third day were dedicated to the memory of the dead, and were filled with all manner of terrors from evil spirits, and the casting of corresponding spells against them. On the fourth day the return of the god was greeted with jubilation. On ship-like carts his picture was carried triumphantly into the city: the protector of the vine had returned to Hellas from the lands of the far East. Many ancient and later works of art have recorded this scene. He is quite often accompanied by Ariadne, whom he found on Naxos, abandoned by Theseus, and took as his wife (Ill. 14).

The wealth of these festivities gave to the world two of the most beautiful of art forms. From the Dithyrambos, a choral song recited during the celebrations of the cult which took its substance from the heroic myth, great poets of the sixth and fifth centuries developed the drama. At the same time from the homespun entertainments, choral performances with dancing and satirical songs, masques and the frequently hilarious staged badinage developed the comedy.

As with so many other things, Rome took over from conquered Greece the festivities connected with Dionysus. Nonetheless, the authorities from the outset adopted strict measures against the more orgiastic aspects of the cult. In 189 B.C. the Senate ordered mass arrests of those taking part in the celebrations. Apparently about seven thousand people were detained, of whom several were executed. But realizing that such a movement was not to be put down by prohibition, the authorities abandoned the attempt to suppress the cult – for it was not, like early Christianity, hostile to the ruling ideology of the state. The participants in the Dionysia were merely obliged to register with the authorities who kept lists of members.

They must have been rather large. For the influence of Eastern ideas on salvation had expanded those beliefs of the Dionysus cult which were connected with his apparent death during the winter and his "distant voyages". In addition came the entwining of the rite with wine, which – equated with Dionysus – was worshipped in hymns as bringer of joy, saviour, and, in drunkenness, also as "liberator of limbs". In harmony with all these points of faith was the dominating idea of the god's "eternal return" – a concept on which the adherents of his cult founded their hopes in a renewed life after death. These ideas found expression in a great many works of art. The elaborate decoration of many sarcophagi is particularly telling. Here we see the god festooned in vines as a boy, or bearded in the full of manhood, surrounded by his human and animal escort. The Casali sarcophagus depicts the moment when Dionysus meets the lonely Ariadne on Naxos (Ill. 17). Other works connected with his cult depict a pair of panthers or birds ordered on each side of a vine springing from an urn (Ill. 19). A Byzantine relief from Corinth possibly recalls some late echo of the cult, with its depiction of a lion eating grapes from a vine: an addiction for

*4 Planting vines. From: Petrus de Crescentiis, Opus ruralium commodorum libri XII, Speyer 1493.*

which the king of the jungle is not generally noted (Ill. 18).

The chief motif in all this art is the vine. It symbolizes the god himself, and with its blossoming, ripening, fruiting and fading is the incarnation of his eternal return. And the vine was to keep this function even after the cult of Dionysus was forced to yield to the state religion of later Christianity. The most striking instance of this is the mosaic in the Mausoleum of St.Constanza in Rome (Ill. 20). The daughter of the emperor, who in history was the first to battle under the sign of the cross, found her resting place amid pagan, Dionysian motifs, whose artistic execution carries on the heritage of Antiquity. Pictorial elements prove that Christianity must for a long time have found a very serious opponent in the ideology of the Dionysus cult, and could only defeat him by adopting some of his essential elements. When we consider the mystic role of wine in the sacrament of the Communion it is no surprise that Dionysian scenes recur in the reliefs on early Christian sarcophagi – with the difference that the old wine god is replaced by the Good Shepherd. How tenacious the ancient models were, both as regards the figure himself and the life of his entourage, is shown by a sarcophagus in the Vatican Museum (Ill. 21).

This symbiosis drew further strength from the traditions of the Bible itself. Its extensive vine and wine symbolism recurred again and again in works of art. We need only recall the leaf and grape motif on the capitals of many churches, the numerous madonnas with grapes, and the representation of Christ in the wine-press.

The starting point for this excursion into the realm of religious beliefs, legends and tales was the observation that the mythological traditions of the Ancients, notwithstanding their fairy-tale exaggerations, might contain thoroughly real elements which could give a key to particular details of the origin and spreading abroad of the culture of the vine. There is for instance the role of women in creating its beginnings, which is time and again confirmed by mythology. It is also significant that a Thracian forest god, one of whose attributes was the wild vine and its fruits, becomes the mystic lord of wine in the ancient Mediterranean world. He comes,

so say the Greeks, on a ship out of the East, to teach them the cultivation and care of the new plant – a piece of information which should engage us further. And finally the experience with that first taste of fermented grape-juice, springing, apparently, from such a peculiar train of circumstances, is worth some further consideration. But to judge the historic substance behind such accounts, we must first outline the discoveries of science about the history of wine-growing.

## 🍇 The Wild Vine

We should first look at the absolute beginnings of winemaking and are at once confounded by certain difficulties. For there are two almost diametrically opposed theories on the matter. One of them, represented above all by the older literature, claims that wine made from grapes was known to man even before he learned to grow crops, and perhaps as early as the end of the last Ice Age. The other theory, supported today by almost all expert opinions, denies this. It reduces the period of planned cultivation of the vine to some six or seven thousand years, and can call, in its own support, on the weight of scientifically grounded arguments.

But those who would like to grant the old Stone-Age hunter a cup of beaded, if not totally fermented grape juice also have some solid proofs. The existence of the vine at this time, and even much earlier, can be easily established. In the Tertiary period, when our brown coal deposits were forming, it covered large areas of Europe. Even Iceland and Greenland bore its green garlands, as did North America as far as Alaska. So did Japan. We know this from the prints of its leaves, pips and woody parts recorded in stone and coal. The advancing glaciers of the Ice Age wiped it out in more northerly regions. As the climate grew milder, about ten thousand years ago, it won back many of its former positions. Its fruit was valuable food for those groups of men who populated western and central Europe during the late Stone Age and the Bronze Age, as well as those in the areas south of the Caucasus and in the Near East. This is proved by discoveries of grape-pips in prehistoric settlements. North and

south of the Alps in the remains of lake dwellings whole clumps of them have come to light. Possibly they are the remains of a simple pressing process. But such discoveries are among the rarities. Most excavations of inhabited strata have found individual pips, and sometimes their impressions in clay fragments. Remains of this sort have been found in northern Italy, Yugoslavia, Greece, and Asia Minor. The world-famous excavations of Troy and Tiryns brought the discovery that in both regions about four thousand years ago the grape was enjoyed as a side dish at lavishly prepared banquets.

But they did not grow in those plantations which Homer had in mind, when over a thousand years later he described the shield of Achilles. They came much more from vines which grew without any intervention on the part of man. This has been established from the excavated grape-pips themselves, by palaeobotany. The shape of these seeds tells the researcher that they once sat in grapes of the wild vine strains (*Vitis vinifera* subsp. *silvestris*, *Vitis caucasica Vav.*). Until well into the second millennium B.C. there are no traces of the seeds of the cultivated vine (*Vitis vinifera* subsp. *sativa*).

Greater or smaller remains of wild vines of the type *Vitis silvestris* are still found today in central France, southwestern Switzerland, the valley of the Upper Rhine, the Danube basin and in southern Ukraine. The Caucasian vine (*Vitis caucasica Vav.*) is dominant in Asia Minor, Transcaucasia and the lands east of there as far as the Hindu Kush. Still other strains are found in North America. Their fruits led to a part of its eastern coast being named "Vinland hit goda", the good Vineland, in about A.D. 1000. An old Icelandic saga recounts how Leif Ericson the Norseman with his people sailed out westwards from Greenland and discovered a new land. He followed the coast southwards, until the shore seemed suitably attractive for a longer stay. They rowed into a river estuary and set up a permanent winter camp. Then Leif divided his crew into two groups, of which one was to stay in the camp, while the other reconnoitred the land in a series of day's excursions. What happened then is best left in the words of the "Saga of the Greenlanders".

"One evening one of the company was missing: it was the German Tyrkir. Leif was much distressed at this, for Tyrkir had been a long time with him and his father, and in his childhood had loved him dearly. Leif summoned his men and set out to look for him. Twelve men were with him. They had gone but a short stretch of the way when Tyrkir came to meet them. They greeted him joyfully.

Leif noticed quickly that his adoptive father was not himself. . . . He asked him: 'Why come you so late, chosen father, and separate yourself from your comrades?' The other for a long time spoke German, rolled his eyes much and made a wry face. None of them could understand what he was saying. After a while he began to speak in the language of the Norsemen, and said: 'I have not been far, and yet I can report a new discovery: I have found vines and grapes.' – 'Is that true, adopted father?' asked Leif. – 'Of course it's true', answered Tyrkir. 'For I grew up in a place where there is no shortage of vines or grapes.'

They slept through the night. But next morning Leif said to his people: 'We must undertake two tasks: on one day collect grapes, and on the next cut vines and fell trees, so that we may have a cargo for our ship.' This was agreed. It is told that the towing boat was soon laden with grapes. Then trees were felled.

When Spring approached they prepared for their departure. Leif gave the land a name after its character, and called it Vinland."

This vivid description gives us, in addition to the event itself, one valuable insight. The grapes of this wild vine must have been indeed tasty, if they could evoke such ecstasy in a German well used to the cultivated fruits of his homeland. This is confirmed by the report of an Italian traveller who five hundred years later was to visit the lands in the Gulf of the St. Lawrence. He found vines there hanging among the trees, and tried their fruits. The result seems to have surpassed all expectations, for he records that if this vine were to be cultivated and tended it would certainly be possible to "make the best wine out of the grapes. For they are sweet and hardly less worthy than our own."

Very similar conclusions were arrived at by others about the fruits of the wild vine of southeast Europe and Transcaucasia. Right up to most recent times over this whole region men collected the grapes, in good years easily fermentable, and prepared wine from them. We have no reason to doubt that the same was done in prehistoric times – especially as ancient authors confirm as much for the regions of the Crimea and fabled Colchis. There are many clues to be got from what one reporter said of the coastal strip of Lower Moesia, more or less the region of the modern Dobruja. An army which had marched into this region fell into dire straits because the country was without lakes, rivers or wells. The thirsty soldiers were saved, however, by the grapes of the wild vine, which almost everywhere festooned the forests. Their abundance was also exploited in much later times by the population of this region, who lived from fishing and cattle-rearing. Even today along this stretch of the Bulgarian Black Sea coast one can find stone slabs of two metres or more in diameter, chiselled out into shallow basins. In these "bowls" the grapes of the wild vine were trodden. The juice flowed through a channel carved in the rim, and was caught in smaller vessels. Similar basins, mostly hollowed in the rocky ground, are also found in Transcaucasia and in some places in the Near East. The function of such basins cannot always be definitely established – unless the discoverer or archeologist finds grape-pips in them. This simple process for getting the juice from grapes was never forgotten completely, even after the domesticated vine had won the field. This is proved by the existence of similar treading troughs in north-eastern Hungary.

Supported by these facts we are surely not far wrong in supposing that the appetizing fruits of various species of wild vine served men as food from earliest times. Observations made over generations taught them where to look for the tastiest, juiciest varieties. The wealth of the Autumn fruit prompted them to consider some way of keeping and preserving the harvest for later use. Drying it in the sun was one way, which recommended itself mostly to the peoples of southern regions. Just at this time may equally have been gathered those first experiences of the fermentation of grape juice and the Persian tales illustrated how suspiciously the result of this process may have been treated. This may not have been the case everywhere, however, for the production of fermented drinks out of wild plants was known to men in earliest times, probably even before the domestication of corn and root vegetables. The necessary juice was got from raspberries, blackberries, wild apples, pears and cherries, and perhaps even from mulberries, elders and sloes. Prehistoric finds confirm this. Men also made a fermented infusion of cow-parsnip using the lactic acid contained in the stem and green parts of this plant. Some Indian peoples of North America had mastered the art of concocting an intoxicating drink out of the sap of the sugar-maple, and the preparation of mead from thinned honey was known almost all over the world. But apart from honey none of these fruits and plants offered such an abundant and good-tasting raw material for fermentation as the ripe grape. That assured it pride of place in wine-making, wherever it could be gathered in sufficient quantities. Not for nothing do the fermented products of other plants also carry the name "wine". We speak of palm wine, parsnip wine, fruit wine, and even, speaking of mead, honey wine – to name but a few examples.

## The Origins and Travels of the Cultivated Vine

Before these coinages could gain a hold the long, painstaking process by which the cultivated vine was developed out of the wild plant had first to be accomplished. How this happened is still a mystery. If we are to believe legends, the achievement was the result of the intervention of divine authorities. It is remarkable how working men in the past continually found such ways of denying their own skills. Yet the result of his labours – particularly in the field which interests us here – are amazing. During thousands of years, by cultivating mutations, as well as by continually crossing selected and especially valuable strains, he managed to create a wealth of different cultivated vines almost inestimable in its abundance. These vines differ from their uncultivated ancestors primarily in being hermaphroditic. Their flowers contain both seeds and stamens, i.e. male and female parts. Wild vines, on the other hand, are mostly divided into the two sexes and only their female

stems can bear fruit. But occasionally they produce the hermaphrodite. In selecting vines for cultivation man probably picked on these because their further development offered fewer difficulties than that of the sexually divided vines.

Wild and cultivated vines also differ to some extent in the living conditions they demand. Our modern vine prefers a stony ground mixed with fine earth, well aired and easily warmed through. The European wild vine, however, grows best in light woodlands with a moist subsoil. A direct line of descent from this variety thus seems hardly probable. The Caucasus vine has still different tastes, flourishing best in dry regions. For this reason it probably played an important role in the development of the cultivated varieties. But the participation of wild vines from further east, or of a later crossing of the European type, cannot be ruled out.

Indeed, it will be difficult to challenge the dominance of Western Asia in the process of domesticating the vine. Apart from the myths surrounding its origins, there are also linguistic facts which support the case, above all the very name of wine itself. Our present knowledge suggests that its root was an ancient, now extinct word from the Caucasian-Black Sea region – *voino*. This meant the intoxicating drink made from grapes. With the secrets of cultivating the vine it was taken over and modified by other languages. Thus the Greeks in very early times were already speaking of *woinos*, the Romans of *vinum*, the Albanians of *vere*. In the Armenian tongue, i.e. near the supposed place of origin, the earliest form changed to *gini*. Most of the modern European names of the noble drink are taken from Latin; an exception is the Hungarian *bor*, which comes from a Turkish language root.

Early, western Asian, vine cultivation was related to the process, older by some thousands of years, of cultivating corn crops. It adopted from it certain basic skills and implements, and in particular the hoe, which is characteristic for wine-growing from the very beginning. Even today, in regions where machinery is not available, or its introduction is impracticable, the hoe, in its multitudinous variations of form, works alongside the mattock, spade and pronged fork, to lay the necessary groundwork for the vine's further progress.

5 *Weeding. From: Petrus de Crescentiis*, Opus ruralium commodorum libri XII, *Speyer 1493.*

## The Gardens of Lagash, Kish and Nineveh

But when and by what routes was the new culture spread abroad?

We must admit from the outset, that our information as to the time and directions of this process is precise only for the last two thousand years. For the preceding period, a great deal must remain conjecture. Our sources here are archaeological finds, old sculptures, and also accounts from myths and sagas, partly preserved in later poetry.

Our oldest reports come from Mesopotamia and the lands of the Nile. They give us a picture of a flourishing wine industry, which has long since progressed from its first, hesitant stages.

In Lagash, one of the ancient Sumerian city-states near the lower course of the Tigris, there were artificially watered gardens where vines and fruit trees bloomed as early as 2,500 B.C. In addition to their own production, their kings ordered imports of wine from the "hills of the East", probably a reference to the regions in the West and South-west of modern Iran. Part of this territory was included in ancient Elam and may be seen as another early centre of wine-growing, if not the actual cradle of vine culture.

That wine trade was very much part of government business is confirmed by cuneiform texts from Kish, another ancient Mesopotamian settlement. They tell us that the fourth of those legendary dynasties to rule the city "after the flood" was founded by Azag-Bau, a lady who traded in wine. It is both surprising and heartening that as early as 5,000 years ago the fate of a great community lay in the hands of a woman. Her experiences in business cannot have come amiss in the governing of the city.

In ancient Mesopotamia and in the mountain lands to the east of it, right as far as Asia Minor, grape wine was the favoured drink of kings, priests and wealthy merchants. It was also considered to be a fitting sacrifice as well as a symbol of blossoming abundance and ripening. In their rock pictures the Hittites decorated their fertility god with corn ears and grapes (Ill. 23). In this they were following a tradition which, in the lands of Asia Minor and Syria, must surely reach back to the period when the vine was taken

into cultivation for the very first time. These lands, too, in all probability, can be counted among the oldest centres of planned wine-growing. The legend from Ugarit, of Pagat's assistance in this work, points in a similar direction. It is not without interest in this connection that the Tree of Life mentioned in the *Gilgamesh Epic* was pictured blooming in western Syria, as a vine plant.

This land was clearly rich in vines at a very early period. Texts on clay tablets record that here, in the middle of the second millennium, there lived in one settlement alone, no fewer than 81 owners of vineyards. The surplus output of these plantations will probably have been sent as an item of trade to Cyprus, Asia Minor and Crete, as well as towards Egypt; routes which the Phoenicians some five hundred years later were to operate with great financial success. When extended they opened up trade with Greece and with the people of the western Mediterranean.

The vineyards of the Assyrian proprietors must also have been of a considerable size. They had taken over the heritage of the "eastern hills" mentioned in the Sumerian sources. A register of properties from the seventh century B.C., from the region of Harran, to the north-west of modern Aleppo, describes plantations of sizes which for those times are quite remarkable. These estates varied in size between 2,000 and 29,000 plants if one can believe the figures quoted. A bas-relief from this time, from Nineveh, reveals that in these vineyards the vines were trained to grow up trees, a process sanctified by tradition (Ill. 24, 25). Doubtless many Assyrian townships were surrounded by such plantations, draped in glowing, juicy green, and, during the Autumn ripening, offering a magnificent display of colour. It is hard to reconcile such a picture with the brutality of warfare as recounted on their clay tablets, and in all its horrible detail, in their sculptures.

The prodigal propensities of the Assyrian kings were preserved for the amazement of posterity in their archives. Ashurnasirpal II, under whose reign Assyria rose in the ninth century B.C. to become the major power of Mesopotamia, celebrated the opening of his new palace, lying amid parkland at Kalach, by hosting his guests with ten thousand skins of

wine. Even if we make some allowance for boastful exaggeration on the part of his chroniclers, the finds which came to light during the excavation of this magnificent fortress, lying below the hill of Nimrud, testify to the fondness of the Assyrian aristocracy for the noble drink. The remains of numerous storage vessels also testify indirectly to the former abundance and prosperity of wine-growing in this part of the Near East.

6 *Bacchus drinking with lyre player.*
*Detail from a Roman mosaic, 2nd–3rd century.*
*Lapidarium Vienne.*

7 *The drunken Dionysus with retinue.*
*Stucco wall from Pompeii, Museo Archeologico*
*Nazionale, Naples.*

8 *Head of a drunken satyr from the Villa*
*dei Papiri, Herculaneum. Bronze, 1st century.*
*Museo Archeologico Nazionale, Naples.*

9 *Dionysian dancing couple in the Tomba delle*
*Leonesse, Tarquinia, 7th century B.C.*

10 *The Drinkers. Painting by Diego de Velázquez (1599–1660). Prado, Madrid.*

11 *Dionysus in the form of grapes at Vesuvius. Wall painting from Pompeii. The volcano still has its shape from before the great eruption of 79. Along its slopes can be seen a* vinea camerata. *Museo Archeologico Nazionale, Naples.*

12 *Head of Dionysus on a silver drachma from Naxos, 550–530 B.C. Collection Leu. Zurich.*

13 *Dionysus visiting a death-bed. Greek sacramental relief. British Museum, London.*

14 *Dionysus meets Ariadne. Painting by*
*Giambattista Cima da Conegliano (1459–1517).*
*Museo Poldi Pezzoli, Milan.*

15 *Bacchus. Carving from the staircase of the*
*Güldenkammer in the Town Hall in Bremen, 1620.*

16 *Amoretti picking grapes, symbolizing Autumn. Relief on the narrow side of the Junius Bassus Sarcophagus, 359. Grotte Vaticane, Rome.*

17 *Dionysus and Ariadne. Relief from a Roman sarcophagus of the 2nd century. Ny Carlsberg. Glyptic Collection, Copenhagen.*

18 *Lion feeding on grapes. Byzantine marble relief. Archeological Museum, Ancient Corinth.*

19 *Dionysian motif: vines flanked by a pair of panthers. Ancient relief, 2nd century, set in the outer wall of the Church of Maria Saal near Klagenfurt.*

20  *Amoretti harvesting and treading grapes. In front of the treading trough can be seen three pithoi buried up to the shoulders. Vault mosaic from the Mausoleum of St. Constanza, Rome. First half of 4th century.*

21 *Christian and Dionysian symbolism on a sarcophagus from late Antiquity, 4th century. Musei Vaticani, Rome.*

22 *The reverse of this Chinese grape mirror from the Tang era (618–907) shows the famous palace dogs – now known as Pekinese – surrounded by a wreath of fruit-laden vines. Museum für Völkerkunde, Leipzig.*

26 Christ in the wine-press. In the lower right-
hand part of the picture barrel-hands are letting
a cask down a ladder into the cellar. Painting,
c. 1500. Bayerisches Nationalmuseum, Munich.

27 The mystic press. Painted window from the
Church of St. Étienne-du-Mont, Paris, created
between 1612 and 1622.

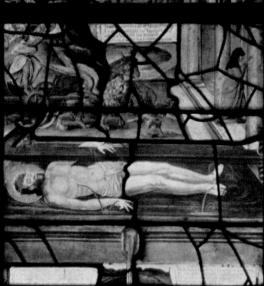

Heureux homme Chrestie li fermement tu crois
Que dieu pour te sauuer a souffert a la croix,
Et que les Sacrements retenus a l'Eglise,
De son sang precieux ont eu commencement
Qui le bien receuront toute offense est remise
Et qu'on ne peut sans eux auoir son sauuement.

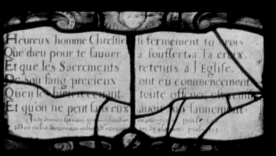

28 *The symbolic vine. Relief on the west door of the Cathedral of Toledo, 15th century.*

29 *Madonna with grape. Cranach studio and school, c. 1526. Wartburg Museum, Eisenach.*

## The Wine List of Li Tai-bo

So far we have been considering only the western frontier of the most ancient centre of vine culture. Equally interesting is its expansion eastwards.

Unhappily, our sources in this region run more sparsely than in the area of the old kingdoms of the Near East. Possibly in this very region much has so far escaped the attention of the researcher, or awaits a final solution. We shall have to make do with the little that piecemeal historical accounts give us.

Ancient China has already been mentioned in connection with the injunctions to abstinence of the mythical Emperor Yü. He forebade the use of rice wine. Thus there was at this time obviously no such thing as a cultivated vine. Neither can we be quite certain which fruit went into the wine celebrated in the first millennium B.C., in the songs and poems of the "Book of Songs" *(Sch'djing)*. Perhaps the later of them refer to the juice of the grape. We can be quite certain, however, that a certain Li Tai-bo (701–762) knew the gift of the vine, and dedicated immortal lines to it.

> "The scent of flowers, and a jug of wine;
> Will no one come to help me as I drink?
> No matter, then: O Moon, I'll drink with
> thee,
> And you, my shadow, keep us company.
> The moon, in truth, for drinking is not
> made,
> My shadow only apes me and pretends,
> But nonetheless, come here, my good old
> friends,
> Come here, good moon, and you, my faithful shade.
> So sing I, and the moon he wags his head.
> I dance, my shadow skitters to and fro.
> For waking we shall share both wine and
> bread
> Then drunken homeward each alone shall
> go.
> But we to heaven shall march in one array,
> There let us meet again, by the Milky
> Way!"

Viniculture was probably known in the Chinese Empire about two thousand years ago. It came to them from the West. This is betrayed by the Chinese word for wine, *pu-tau*, which comes most probably fom the Persian *budawa* (grape). This fact links us with one of the early centres of vine culture. The vine may have found its way over the ancient central Asian caravan routes, on which the Fergana valley, known since Antiquity for the abundance of its vines, may have formed a stopping-place. Further east, archeologists excavating the ruined city of Loulan under its cover of desert sand found the remains of vines. Unless appearances deceive, they were planted here at the time of the Han dynasty. Wu-di (146–86 B.C.), the most important ruler of this line, definitely supervised the planting of vines. Buddhist monks were responsible for the spread of wine-growing between the fourth and eighth centuries along the Tarim basin. With the arrival of Islam the vine disappeared from this region. But in compensation it moved eastwards to the provinces of Shantung and Djangsu, by the Yellow Sea.

## Vines on Fujiyama

Exported from China, wine-growing found its way to Japan a good thousand years ago. A sure indication of its origin is again the name of the grape, which in Japanese has become further modified to *budo*.

But even before this the islands of the Far East already had their own variety of wild vine, which went by the name *ebi*. Nowadays it persists, above all, in mountain regions. Its small, nearly black fruits were used to provide a deep purple juice for the dying of textiles. The first cultivated vineyards of any importance were apparently founded in about 1200, in what is now the prefecture of Yamanashi at the foot of Fujiyama. A peasant from the village of Ivasaki (Ivai) is said to have provided the impulse for this by finding a vine plant at the roadside, on his way home from the temple, and planting it in his garden. The vine repayed this kindness so well that he was shortly in a position to regale one of the foremost princes of the land with three baskets full of grapes.

Japanese wine-growing took a significant upturn in the course of the seventeenth century. The technique of training the vines up bamboo poles was introduced at this time. About the same period, it is believed, new varieties were brought over from the mainland. It was not until 1879 that Japanese wine-growers were introduced to European and American cultivated vines.

## Side Shoots in India

According to the legends of the Ancient Greeks, it was Dionysus himself who carried the vine to India. But there is no need to trouble the god with such a journey. It seems far more probable that the cultivated vine had already spread during prehistoric times from the uplands of western Asia to the lands beyond the Indus. Its fruits were known there as early as 2,500 years ago. Whether they were eaten as grapes or pressed remains a matter for conjecture. Alcoholic drinks made from rice, sugar-cane or fruits were not unknown in India at this time, and there were even specially organized selling places. None the less, the area of the subcontinent given over to wine-growing has remained modest right up to the present day. In central and southern India, and above all in the states of Maharashtra, Mysore and Andhra Pradesh, it covers no more than an area of about seven thousand five hundred hectares.

In the course of thousands of years vine culture beat a prodigious path right across Asia. Tended and carried further by busy hands, it spread eastwards from its birthplace through ninety degrees of longitude and almost five thousand miles. The first limit to its expansion was the Pacific, and even here it ventured the leap over to the Japanese islands.

## And Noah Became Drunk

To the West there were no such boundaries to block the advance of the vine. Here the land between the Mediterranean and the Arabian desert made a bridge for its further march. The plant of Dionysus forged a peaceful path of conquest across it. Although innocent of any ambitions to make history, it still wove in the history of human industry a golden thread, in which many a bright story sparkles.

The first of these took place in this very land bridge between Asia and Africa, in Palestine. Or rather – if we are to believe the first book of Moses – in Armenia, at the foot of Mount Ararat. There where the monastery of Etshmiadsin now stands, our ancestor Noah planted the first vineyard in world history, after the safe landing of the ark at the end of the Flood. The Bible thus locates with amazing accuracy the oldest centre of vine-growing. What happened when Noah tested his first vintage is, accordingly, all the more distressing.

"And he drank of the wine, and became drunk, and lay uncovered in his tent.

And Ham, the father of Canaan, saw the nakedness of his father, and told his two brothers outside.

Then Shem and Japheth took a garment, laid it upon both their shoulders, and walked backward and covered the nakedness of their father; their faces were turned away, and they did not see their father's nakedness.

When Noah awoke from his wine and knew what his youngest son had done to him, he said, 'Cursed be Canaan; a slave of slaves shall he be to his brothers.'"

The fine arts have often taken up this story, sometimes in epic style, like the mosaic in the vestibule of San Marco's (Ill. 40), or not infrequently concentrating on the evil deed of Ham.

Ham as a result of this affair was banished to the desert. But among his children was Canaan, whose tribe peopled the Promised Land and made it fertile, so that it flowed with milk and honey. And the success with which Ham's grandson and great-grandson also tended wine-growing is demonstrated by the giant grapes which Joshua and Caleb brought to the descendents of Shem from the Promised Land (Ill. 37, 38, 39). Thus they too made good use of the treasures of Canaan, whose masters after bitter struggles they were to become.

Although history is not a family drama of guilt and sin, the Biblical legend does reflect, much distorted, a number of truths. It is certain that wine-growing in Palestine can boast a long history. Just as in Syria, there are regions here where treading troughs were carved into the bedrock. The system of extracting grape-

30 *Noah sleeping under the vine. Woodcut from the Herbal of Hieronymus Bock, Strasbourg 1546.*

juice associated with these could have been developed while men were still harvesting the fruits of the wild vine. The vine and wine appear repeatedly as symbols in the holy scriptures of the early Jews, and testify to the important part played by vine culture in their agriculture. For information about early Palestinian wine-growing the Bible itself remains a valuable source. At the same time the Jews, if we take their traditions at face value, had already learnt the cultivation and care of the vine before their entry into the lands of the Canaanites. For they were led there out of a land where the art had been mastered to a high degree of perfection for several thousand years, from Egypt.

## Vine Bowers by the Nile

If we were to attribute the origins of wine-growing to the place where it is first mentioned in written records, we would have to accord the honour to the Nile Delta. Here during the period of the Old Kingdom, about 5,000 years ago, it was already in full bloom. Hieroglyphic texts from first dynasty graves reveal this, speaking of "the wine-presses of the eastern and western lands", with which the grapes that grew around the Mareotis Sea and Tanis were probably pressed. The large number of jars of wine interred along with the bodies of kings give further early evidence about ancient Egyptian vine culture. The necropolises of the rulers and their officials from the New Kingdom, about 3,500 years ago, contain paintings which give us detailed insights into the ways that vines were then grown, the grapes picked and pressed, and the wine stored, in the lands along the banks of the Nile. They also show us that the higher nobility indulged in the fermented juice without moderation – more than they could keep down. Women, too, were present at these drinking bouts. They kept pace with the men, and then shared the discomfiture caused by an over-charged stomach. The idea of the Nile lands being peopled by beer drinkers thus needs to be revised, especially as far as concerns the habits of its top ten thousand.

We can only estimate when the cultivated vine was brought to Egypt. By about 3,000 B.C. it was already established in the north of the country. Thus it must have been received out of the East some time in prehistory. Perhaps it was brought by early migrants, who were later absorbed into the Egyptian people as it emerged.

Old texts frequently refer to the high perfection of wine-growing in the lands east of the ancient Nile lands and of the Sinai Peninsula. One Sinuhe, who at the beginning of the second millennium B.C. lived as a courtier at the palaces of Pharaoh Sesostris I, related from his own experience that "there the wine was more abundant than water". The armies of the Old Kingdom had made similar discoveries some five hundred years earlier than this, when they advanced into the northern part of Sinai and devastated there the vines and fig trees of the "sand dwellers". Details like these point us the path of the vine on its way from western Asia to the Nile. They also show us at how early a date wine-growing was established and flourishing in Palestine and Syria.

## Outpost Carthage

There remains the question of whether the vine pressed on further westwards, from Egypt through North Africa. This would not have been impossible. A path along the coast offered itself, or perhaps one further inland, for five thousand years ago these lands had not yet become the steppes and deserts that make them seem so hostile to settlement today. But for either direction of migration we have no definite proofs.

And yet the princely merchants of ancient Carthage possessed extensive vineyards. There was even a treatise on vine culture written by Mago, one of their most notable representatives. It circulated in the ancient world and was not without influence on the ideas of Roman authors writing on the subject. Sadly it has not survived to the present day. But in any case we have no reason to doubt the existence of a highly-developed wine industry long before the arrival of the Romans in this part of North Africa.

There is, however, no compelling reason to make Egypt responsible for its spread there. For the Carthaginians could also have brought the necessary skills and cuttings with them, directly from the place whence they had set out as colonists, from their Phoenician homeland. Along the coasts of Palestine and Syria wine had, for a long time, been a favourite export. Why, then, when founding new settlements, should they neglect the vine as a guarantee of future wealth? The settlers' ships will probably have brought with them all the cuttings they needed to secure the basis for new plantations.

Did the vine's travels take it even further west from here – perhaps to the Phoenician settlements on Sicily and along the coast of the Iberian peninsula? It is a tempting idea, even though we have no evidence to prove such an early transplanting of the vine. But neither can we exclude the possibility of such an attempt being made.

## Greek Wine-growers and Colonists

Phoenicia, according to legend, was also the source from which Greece learned vine culture. Accounts to this effect were based chiefly on the fact that Greek cities since early times had made very welcome the seafaring merchants from Byblos, Tyre and Sidon. But long before wine ships were putting out for Greece from these distant shores, men there were already familiar with the ordered cultivation of the vine. Evidence of this is the grape-pips found in excavations at Orchomenos. They come unmistakably from cultivated vines. They can be dated around the middle of the second millennium, when gold-rich Mycenae assumed prominence in the Peloponnese. The beautifully-formed cups and bowls from excavated treasures may thus have once held home-produced wine – which does not exclude the possibility that in the citadels of that age feasting princes also enjoyed Aegean imports. In addition the fruits of the wild vine were still utilized. This is shown by grape-pips from Tiryns, neighbour to Mycenae in space and time. For the men of those times, the double nature of Dionysus – defender of the fruits and animals of the forest but also of the cultivated vine – would have seemed no contradiction at all.

In the subsequent development of Greek wine-growing, influences from Asia Minor and possibly from Crete probably played a part. Such connexions were already established as a result of the migration to the coast of Asia Minor, at the turn of the second and first millennia, of numerous Ionians and Aeolians from the Greek mainland, driven out by the Dorians penetrating from the North. There they found a highly-developed vine culture, which they made their own and then carried further. Their particular achievement was the perfection of a method of training the vines. They were probably the first to invent the method of cultivation where each individual vine is equipped with one or several supports up which it climbs. This method improves the output from each plant, as well as the good order of the vineyard. It therefore facilitates the systematic, thorough tilling of the soil – one of the first conditions for improving the harvest.

The Greeks also invented the tool which first made stake cultivation really possible. Until then the extraneous suckers had been cut off each year using a simple curved knife. The new method of cultivation demanded an improved implement, whose most important feature was a hatchet-like little blade, added on to the curved back of the cutting tool (Ill. 47, 84). The Roman agriculturalist Columella called this addition *securis*. Subsequently the title "knife with securis" established itself for this kind of tool – to distinguish it from the simple curved knife, known to the Romans as *falx* or *sicilis*. The perfected tool came into use in many places with the spread of wine-growing to the west of the Rhine and south of the Danube, but continued to share the field with the *sicilis* variety. The "knife with securis" predominated in Italy and Friedrich von Bassermann-Jordan, who at the beginning of this century first noticed and established historically the difference in outline and function of this implement, described it as the Italian vine knife.

With its settlement in Greece, wine-growing on a larger scale found a foothold in European territory for the first time. It found in the countrymen of ancient Hellas a good, industrious and inventive guardian to protect and encourage its further progress. The Greek farmer persuaded it to flourish in all the suitable regions of his country (a fact demonstrated by the high profits of Athenian and Corinthian wine traders).

In the wake of colonizing ventures between the eighth and sixth centuries B.C. he took his vines and the secrets of their cultivation to the coast of the western Mediterranean, to Sicily, Italy, southern France and perhaps as far as the Iberian peninsula. Our present state of knowledge does not allow us to say whether and where they met with earlier plantations. We have to consider such a possibility in the case of Siciliy and part of Spain, as well as for several parts of central Italy, where the Etruscans had established their city-states. All of these territories may have learned the secret of wine-growing a few hundred years earlier, from the Near East.

The Greek settlers quickly developed wine-growing wherever their new colonies took root. This is especially true of Sicily, the southern half of Italy and southern France. Herodotus called Bruttium and Lucania "the land of the vine-stakes" *(Oenotria)*, and Sophocles praised Sicily as "Dionysus's darling land". Together with southern Italy it became one of the most important wine-growing centres of the Mediterranean. The output of its plantations is indicated by evidence from the colony of Sybaris on the Gulf of Taranto, founded in 709 B.C. by the Achaeans. Its citizens, proverbial for the luxuriousness of their lives – one of them is thought to have written the first cookery book in world history – had gone so far as to build a system of underground conduits to bring wine for export direct from its cellars to the harbour. Acragas, another Greek colony in southern Sicily, enjoyed within a short time of its foundation a reputation as one of the main suppliers of wine and oil to Carthage.

Of particular importance in the spread of wine-growing was Massalia, present-day Marseilles. It was founded by settlers who arrived from Phocaea on the coast of Asia Minor, in about 600 B.C. Numerous wine amphorae excavated in the valley of the upper Saône and in the French Jura, indicate the range of their trading activities. But the thirsts of the Celts who lived in these regions were soon not to be satisfied by imports brought from overseas, and the people of the lower Rhône got down to growing the wine themselves. Soon the Languedoc as far as the Cevennes was filled with vineyards. The present-day wine-growing regions of the Midi and the Côtes du Rhône had their beginnings at

*31 Wine-grower with dagger and pruning knife. Drawing by Urs Graf (c. 1485–1527).*

this time. And yet the importance of this Greek bridgehead was even greater. For it was from here that in Roman times vine culture travelled out along the great trade routes, in one direction to the Gironde, in another to Burgundy. Here lived the Celtic tribe of the Allobroges, who gave their name to a type of vine. But it is more than doubtful whether the *vinum picatum* made from it, with its pitchy flavour, stood in direct lineal connection with the noble Burgundy wines of Yonne and the Côte d'Or. But its title allows us to suppose that it was stored and transported in tarred barrels, even though the discovery of these is generally attributed to the Gauls.

## 🍇 *Wine in Business and Politics: Rome*

The Romans who conquered the land promoted wine-growing. With their own needs in mind they supported the enclosure of suitable country. Thus at the beginning of our era the vine became a prized plant to the North of Burgundy as well. In the following centuries we find it in Alsace and in the bordering regions of North Switzerland, in the Palatinate and on the banks of the Mosel and the Ahr. It followed the Roman armies, merchants and colonists into Germany left of the Rhine.

It even seems that they attempted to grow wine in cool and rainy England. Near the foundations of a Roman villa in Hertfordshire to the North of London excavations revealed remains of vine plants on a slope facing southwest. Perhaps the fruit from this plantation was served only as a rather sour dessert. But we cannot discount the possibility that it was pressed. In any case, this discovery proves the existence, albeit on a modest scale, of Roman vine-growing north of the Channel.

Greater success attended efforts to find the vine more land to the East of the Adriatic. Along the coast, earlier plantations stemming from Greek roots were discovered. But the Romans, it seems, deserve the credit for expanding vine cultivation as far as the Danube, and handing on the new culture to the tribes and peoples of Illyria, Pannonia, Noricum and Raetia.

In the Iberian peninsula the Roman conquerors were at first only interested in putting down new plantations of Italian vines. Their sources tell us nothing of the wine which had been grown there, possibly since very early times. Perhaps the new rulers simply did not like it, for following the conquest of the country they set up a rather remarkable office, whose holder enjoyed the title "Procurator for furthering the cultivation of Falernum vines in the province of Baetica". He was responsible for seeing that the region on both sides of the river Baetis – now known as the Guadalquivir – was planted with cuttings from the then most highly-esteemed wine-growing area of Italy. Baetica corresponds roughly to the modern wine-growing region of Jerez. The Phoenicians, some nine hundred years earlier than the Romans, had drawn it into their trading empire on account of its wealth of silver. But the grapes, from whose juice the famous Sherry comes, do not grow on descendants of the vines from Falernum. Newer varieties provide us with that joy.

The procurator's success can be seen in the trade figures. Spanish wines, on account of their competitive prices, flooded the Roman and Italian market in the imperial era. By about the middle of the second century twenty million amphorae are thought to have been shipped to the ports of the Italian peninsula. In modern figures that would be a good 500 million litres: a figure which says much for the energy of the Spaniards and the thirsts of the Romans. (Nowadays Spain and Portugal together export something like 750 million litres of wine per year on average.) The regions under cultivation extended even during Antiquity far beyond the province of Baetica. Wine-growing estates at this period had already spread along the whole of the east coast of Spain and as far as the Balearic islands.

Such an overwhelming supply, swelled even further by imports from Gaul, Greece, western Asia and North Africa, must in the long run have worked against the interests of Italian estate owners. The produce of their own vineyards, for the most part tended by slaves, was a major source of income for them. It comes as no surprise then, that as early as the republican era, the Senate, acting as the representative of this class, attempted to ban by law the growing of wine in the provinces of the Empire lying outside Italy, or at least to limit it. We do not know whether these attempts met with any success. Towards the end of the first century, however, the situation had deteriorated still further, and this time in Italy, too. The vine was driving out corn. Vineyards were spreading everywhere at the cost of wheatfields. In A.D. 91 Emperor Domitian had no option but to publish a decree forbidding all further changeovers of land from corn to wine-growing in Italy. The provinces came in for even more drastic treatment. They had to reduce their area of land under the vine by half.

The greatest beneficiary of this regulation was the Italian wine industry and the wine trade, although the success of the law was probably limited, both in duration and in extent. The Emperor himself, according to his critical biographer Suetonius, took no serious steps to guarantee its implementation. In southern Gaul and in southern Spain a little was done *pro forma*, to preserve the appearance of obedience, but in Asia Minor it was universally ignored. The order was probably effective only in the North African provinces, although these no longer played an important role in the Empire's wine trade.

On paper at least, the prohibition continued in force for almost two hundred years. It was only revoked by Emperor Probus, who ruled the Roman Empire between 276 and 282. Grateful tradition has credited him for this with the founding of viniculture on the Rhine and in northern Austria. But in fact cultivated vines had been growing here for a very long time. The death of this ruler, by profession a soldier, was rather tragic. It seems that after a life spent fighting the Persians, Vandals, Franks and Alemannen war had become deeply repugnant to him. He therefore encouraged his armies to indulge in peaceful reconstruction work, which considerably outraged the legionaries, trained in death and destruction. One day, while he was inspecting one of his legions as they were setting up a vineyard in Sirmium, in the region of modern Serbia, they seized the opportunity to attack and murder him.

This violent deed is symbolic for the fate of wine-growing, coming as it does at the beginning of an era which treated the vine more as an object of plunder than as the benevolent rewarder of peaceful toil. In the centuries of the great migrations that followed, the acreage of vineland in nearly all parts of Europe withered away. A similar fate awaited Africa, western and central Asia during the first stormy expansion of Islam. For the Prophet categorically prohibited his followers from all enjoyment of wine. The vine's survival in these regions was only secured because fresh and dried grapes were considered a delicacy. Later on, Mohammed's injunction was taken rather less literally – fortunately enough, for otherwise we should never have been bequeathed the songs of Hafis.

We have to thank the pertinacity and toil of wine-growers for the fact that Europe's old vine culture survived at all, despite the work of fire and sword, and albeit in restricted boundaries. We can imagine how often their vines were prematurely stripped of fruit, or simply hacked down. But they never gave up working to make them blossom again. We should surely set such dogged courage higher than all the victories of great rulers and their armies.

Their toil did not go unrewarded. About the year 1000 the vine was in possession of almost all its former territories, with wine-growers enclosing new lands into the bargain. The Middle Ages were to be its second golden age. As early as the sixth century the clearing of the forests of Burgundy had begun, with vineyards being laid out on the newly-won land. In the Île-de-France, too, the vine gained new ground. An official record of 814, the year of Charlemagne's death, lists plantations to the north, west and south of Paris. Up to the eleventh century the vine continued to extend its hold on the banks of the Scheldt and Meuse in modern Belgium. Vineyards were also planted in the duchies of Brabant and Limburg.

The Venerable Bede, the earliest church historian in the British Isles, tells that in Ireland at the turn of the seventh and eighth centuries there was no shortage of vines. Later reporters sought them there in vain, but none the less found thoroughly respectable plantations in England. Alfred the Great towards the end of the ninth century issued a law aimed at their protection. The Norman Conquest of 1066 did not extinguish wine-growing. Twenty years after this invasion the existence of 39 vineyards was officially recorded although their actual number must have been higher. William Younger, an outstanding expert on the subject, has proved the existence of 139 vineyards in medieval England.

From the ninth century an element of south-eastern origin enriched wine-growing in Europe. It came with the ancestors of the Bulgars and Hungarians, who handed on a form of vine culture, probably developed in Transcaucasian and Iranian territory, that subsequently spread from there to the north of the Black Sea and the Danube.

One of its most characteristic features, as established by the Hungarian ethnographer István Vincze, was the winning of the must without a mechanical press. This process, an old one in terms of historical development, survived to the end of the last century in the north-eastern part of Hungary. One hundred years ago the grapes for the celebrated Tokay were still trodden by foot.

However, wine-growing to the left of the Rhine and south of the Danube continued the Graeco-Roman tradition of pressing with a mechanical press. Its continuity was maintained by the Roman or Romanized peoples of these regions who passed on their skills to the Frankish and Alemann peasants. Many words in the German language connected with wine-growing and cellarage reflect some memory of those times.

To give just some examples: the German word *Wein* (wine) comes from *vinum*, *Most* (must) from *mustum*, *Kelter* (press) from *calcatorium*, *Kufe* (cask) from *cupa* and *Winzer* (wine-grower) from *vinitor*. And the proverbial German *Kaufmann* (merchant) can be traced back finally to *caupo* – a word applied in ancient Rome to publicans and wine-merchants. We can see what the Germans were quick and eager to buy from abroad!

### The Long March North and East

In the lands to the East of the Rhine, wine-growing was introduced during the seventh and eighth centuries. Without doubt there are connections between this process and the Christianization of the west Germanic tribes. Members of monasteries, as well as of the lower clergy, brought to many regions their first acquaintance with wine-growing. The results are donations of vine land preserved in early records: 670 at Bötzingen near the Kaiserstuhl, 716 at Freiburg in Breisgau, 770 at Münnerstadt and Halsheim in Franconia, 776 at Klingenberg, which was later to achieve great fame on account of its red wine, and 780 around Würzburg. The vine was imported to northern Switzerland again in the eighth and ninth centuries. Towards the end of the tenth century wine was being grown on the Werra in South-west Thuringia, and from the end of the eleventh century also on the Saale. The vine had pressed further east as far as the Elbe by the second half of the twelfth century at the latest. At almost the same time there were successful attempts to establish it in the soil of Brandenburg, Silesia and Pomerania. In the lands of the Teutonic Order vineyards are first recorded in documents in 1338. Whether the produce of these regions was acceptable without some moderating additive remains conjectural. The habit of mixing wine with honey, for the benefit of those used to products ripened under a warmer sky, is suggested by an episode from about this same period. When in 1363 Duke Rudolph of Bavaria was visiting the Grand Master at his residence at Marienburg (Malbork), a brew from the Torun hills was set before him. Contrary to all expectations, he found it to be "real oil, that gums up one's mouth". With all the good will in the world – this must have been a case of mixing. Hitherto the fame of this *Thorner* had been so widely recounted that about the same period an abbot from Courland requested the Order, in return for some hunting falcons, to send a cask of it to him, because his own grapes had not ripened well in that particular year. It is evident that the vine was tried out even much further to the North.

From the fourteenth century a further stimulus to the extension of wine-growing in central Europe was provided by economic processes. These included a decline in the price of corn, and a fall in population caused by the repeated outbreaks of plague. Landowners, as well as simple farmers, saw special crops as more attractive and promising of higher rewards. Included with flax, hops, madder, fruit and all kinds of vegetables was, of course, the vine.

Thus it happened that during the fifteenth and sixteenth centuries, vineyards were planted even in those areas which nowadays hardly ever see a grape on the vine. Going down the Rhine the vine reached Xanten, Münster, Göttingen, the southern limits of Holstein, Mecklenburg, Pomerania as well as West and East Prussia. Thuringia and the Electorate of Saxony were at this time flourishing wine provinces, with an area given over to the vine of, apparently, not much less than ten thousand hectares. Erfurt, for example, was ringed by a garland of vines which at the beginning of the Thirty Years' War still covered more than a thousand hectares. And in Dresden, craft workers were at times earning more from retailing their own wines, and those delivered by peasants as payment, than from their professional work.

Even Denmark became the scene of experiments with wine-growing in the second half of the sixteenth century. Its king, the brother-in-law of the Saxon Elector, begged him to send over some cuttings for planting a vineyard. The request was answered twice, in 1560 and 1581, when gifts from Dresden were sent down the Elbe to Hamburg and from there by land across the border. The subsequent fate of the vines remains a mystery. But if they should have thrived sufficiently for their grapes to ripen, their wine will have gone like a saw down the throats of its hardy drinkers. For such was the reputation of the produce of Brandenburg, itself from much further south:

"Vinum de Marchica terra
Transit guttur tamquam serra."

### Recession

The Danish episode marks the culminating point in the spread of wine-growing across Europe. From the second half of the sixteenth

*32 Grape-picking from stakes. From: Petrus de Crescentiis,* Opus ruralium commodorum libri XII, *Speyer 1493.*

century the vine began to retreat from the North and East. It had been tried too hard. Above all it suffered from the cold. On the far side of the 52nd parallel it ripened only under particularly favourable weather conditions, which was more by far than could be expected every year.

On top of this came other negative factors. War destroyed countless vineyards, and fresh battles hindered their re-planting. At the same time the spread and development of long-distance trading provided the northern wines with stiff competition, from wines of superior quality from around the Mediterranean, as well as from the Rhine, Franconia and Swabia. In these regions the area given over to the vine actually increased. Around Stuttgart, for example, it grew between 1550 and 1620 by more than 300 hectares, about 750 acres.

An overwhelming challenger was beer – not that beer made its first appearance in the cellar at this period, it had shared a place with the juice of the grape for hundreds of years before. But in contrast to wine it offered more stable and, in the long run, also higher profits from duties on drink, a fact which no town council and no state administration chose to neglect. Barley successfully challenged the position of the grape, with results that changed the drinking habits of whole regions. Thus Lower Bavaria, which remained committed wine territory into the seventeenth century, began slowly but surely to go over to beer.

On the tables of the nobility and richer burghers a different change took place. Alongside sweet wine, more different drinks from southern lands began to appear: coffee, cocoa and tea. The gathering volume of imports drove prices down and thus helped them to gain wider popularity. Taken with sugar they proved to the liking of the public, who also appreciated their stimulating effect. The bitter, home-grown wines were left standing. At best they were utilized as a basis for spiced drinks in the style of vermouth and punch.

With the progressive relaxation of internal German custom duties and the development of the railway network in the nineteenth century, the fate of the vine was finally settled in such areas as Brandenburg, West Prussia, and extensively too in Silesia, Saxony and Thuringia.

Good wines, now free of additional duty, came on the market everywhere under the same conditions. Similar processes had the same results in France.

Phylloxera, too, left its mark. It hit all wine-growing regions with about the same intensity, but the rehabilitation of vineyards in previously neglected marginal areas was slow in coming, or was not even attempted. Wine-growing in England was at this time still only a faint memory. Only in recent years have successful steps been taken to repatriate the vine north of the Channel. But the loss of territory which the vine suffered in Europe was more than made up for by its migration overseas.

## Across the Oceans

The beginnings of this movement took place almost unnoticed, often accompanied by the din of battle. This is particularly true with the early wine industry of South America. Initially the conquering Spaniards and Portuguese were concerned to hinder all and any plantations there, being anxious to dispose of their own produce as advantageously as possible, in exchange for the apparently inestimable treasures of the New World. In Brazil, Chile and Uruguay they did in fact manage to maintain their monopoly in wine for a very long time. The conditions for change were only created by the anti-colonial, revolutionary movements of the first third of the nineteenth century. With the throwing-off of Spanish and Portuguese rule in these countries, the way was opened for the setting up of their own vine cultures. In other countries of Latin America the agents of Lisbon and Madrid had altogether less success in enforcing their governments' will. As early as the mid-sixteenth century the vine came to Peru, Bolivia and Mexico with the Conquistadores. A short time later Jesuit priests were planting it in Argentina. But in these countries too we can, by and large, only speak of a genuine, profitable blossoming of vine-growing from the nineteenth century onwards.

Spanish priests brought the cultivated vine to California about three hundred years ago, to meet their needs for wine for the mass. Today that State produces about 90 per cent of all the grapes grown in the U.S.A. The rest comes

33 *Breaking the soil. From: Petrus de Crescentiis,* Opus ruralium commodorum libri XII, *Speyer 1493.*

from the State of New York (where wine-growing became known in the early nineteenth century, thanks to Swiss and German immigrants), also from Arkansas, Michigan, Ohio, Pennsylvania and Washington. Even Canada has its own vine region in the province of Ontario near the Niagara Falls. German settlers planted the first cuttings there in 1811.

The Cape wine district in the utmost South of Africa, owes its founding to French religious refugees and German emigrants from the Rhine. They arrived there after the middle of the seventeenth century. The Huguenots, forced to flee their country by the revocation of the Edict of Nantes, settled in the region of Drakensberg and planted their vineyards there. Today this area forms a centre of quality wine-growing in the coastal region.

Australia, the youngest of the continents in the history of discovery, was first introduced to the vine in 1788, when some trial cuttings were planted near Sydney. The experiment, like another one undertaken some 25 years later, does not seem to have met with particular success. A vineyard was established only in 1830, in Camden, forty kilometers to the south-west of Sydney; but this venture was conducted with scientific attention to detail. In 1831, in order to find the most suitable vine for the region, a palette of 574 French and Spanish varieties was planted in New South Wales. To these were added in 1837 the Riesling, introduced by Rheingau growers from near the famous Johannisberg.

With this the vine, like so many other domesticated plants, became a native of all five continents. Beginning in western Asia, the hands of hard-working men carried it over six thousand years around the whole world. Wherever it could, it repaid their toil with abundant fruit. Nowadays, some ten million hectares of the earth's surface is planted with vines. More than half of this acreage lies in Italy, Spain, France and the Soviet Union. The total cultivated area produces a yearly average output of well over 250 million hectolitres of wine.

(Note: 1 hectare = 2.471 acres and 1 hectolitre = 100 litres, nearly 135 standard bottles.)

## Five Thousand Varieties of Noble Vines

The must, or juice, for all this wine is won from an almost inestimable abundance of varieties. The rearing of a cultivated vine did not lead to a kind of "proto-vine" from which all the modern types were to be developed. The beginning was much more a horde of varieties, from which the wine-grower in the course of time extracted new and ever-better strains. This process of selection became increasingly planned, and today is by no means finished, for an army of researchers are constantly seeking to breed new varieties of the vine. This is done partly by exploiting sudden changes in a plant's hereditary features – so-called mutations – and partly by crossing existing varieties. The search is for a higher and better output of grapes which ripen earlier, from plants increasingly resistant to diseases and pests.

The result of thousands of years' endeavour in this direction is an assortment of about five thousand varieties of noble vine. Telling them apart is a science in itself, known to the initiated as ampelography. Scholars of many lands work to introduce clarity and systematic order into this multiplicity of varieties.

Many questions, however, remain as yet unanswered. We would, for example, be pleased to know whether any – and which – varieties of vine have survived until today from ancient times. What was the further fate of the Allobrogian vine which produced the *vinum picatum*? What is its relation to the Burgundy vine? And which vines grew in the famous wine district of Falernum to the South of Rome?

In these and in many other matters we still lack precise information. For although the vine has maintained its outer appearance unchanged over thousands of years, with its roots, runners and leaves, its different varieties have a capacity for change which is quite bewildering. There is also the problem that the most stalwart of them reappear under all manner of different names. Who, apart from the expert, would know that Riesling, Klingelberger and Niederländer are one and the same variety? From country to country, and even from region to region, they carry different names. Our text books on wine-growing list more than a dozen such synonyms for the more important varieties – and such lists are not exhaustive.

Not the least important explanation for this multiplicity of names is the vine's great sensitivity to changes in its natural environment. A different soil and/or a different climate will produce different wines from the same plant – to put things briefly and a little roughly. This discovery has often been made at the cost of hard experience, as the Romans were among the first to find out. What they attempted was the transplantation of vines from Gaul to Italy. The result was a failure. The plants took to their new home poorly or not at all. How often, too, have men tried to transplant to other regions the same set of vine varieties from which Tokay is produced. All their hopes of obtaining vintages of the same quality in a new area have been disappointed. Whoever wishes to enjoy the genuine king of wines has to get it from the hills of Hegyalja, as did the Russian tsars since early times, and with them the kings of France and the emperors of Germany.

Let us pause awhile in our greatest vineyards and look at some of the best-known varieties of vine. We can start with those whose great age has to all intents and purposes been firmly established.

The Muscatels make up a whole "family" in themselves. The large number of sub-varieties indicates a very long history. Their earliest known ancestor seems to have been the psithic vine of the ancient Greeks, from the grapes of which they made chiefly heavy raisin wines. The Roman name *apiana* – the bee vine – is doubtless a reference to the sweet aroma of the grapes. At the same time the name Muscat or Muscatel, which established itself from the Middle Ages onwards, reflects the nutmeg flavour (German *Muskat* = nutmeg) of the grape's succulent flesh. Nowadays we distinguish a yellow strain from the less widely-cultivated blue strain. They give good-quality wines which are strongly aromatic. Muscatel grapes also provide the basis of many dessert wines and, in Italy, Asti Spumante.

The Gutedel variety is thought to have been known to the ancient Egyptians. Experts claimed to have recognized it in the sculptures of the Pharaohs' tombs at Luxor. Today, at the oasis of Fayum, seventy miles to the South-west

of Cairo, it is still bearing rich fruit. Others see its home in Asia Minor, from where a French diplomat is supposed to have brought it to western Europe. According to a third opinion it has blossomed since earliest times in the vineyards of France, and originally in the village of Chasselas near Mâcon – hence the name it goes by in that country. Perhaps all three theories have an element of truth in them, for the Gutedel in its white and red varieties is more widespread than almost any other vine. It is grown in nearly all wine-producing countries, under the most varied names (Chasselas, Krachmoster, Rosmarintraube, Queen Victoria, Raisin d'Officier, Sasla biala, Tribiano tedesco, Doborozne, Fehér ropoós Fabian, and others besides). The tastiness of its fruit makes them favourite table grapes. Pressed and fermented they give a light, smooth, harmonious wine which is low in acids.

In contrast with their abortive experiment with the vines of Gaul, the Romans had considerable success in transplanting the Elbling from its southern home to regions on the left of the Rhine. With its white, blue and red varieties it is probably a descendent of *Vitis albuelis*, described by Pliny in the first century. In his day it was popular as an abundant white wine variety. In central Europe it still produces heavy harvests, albeit of no more than average quality, which are made into light, rather short-lived wines. For this reason quality-conscious landowners have been trying since the Middle Ages to restrict its cultivation. But even today in the vineyards of smaller farmers the Elbling is certainly no rarity.

Of greater age, probably, than the Roman dominion in Gaul is the Gamay Beaujolais. To the present day it has remained, in its many varieties, the most widely cultivated red vine in France. At least a tenth of all wine land – 150–160,000 hectares – is planted with it. In first place comes Beaujolais itself, where it was helped to literary fame by Gabriel Chevallier with his novel *Clochemerle* (1934); then the regions of Mâcon, Châlon and the Côte d'Or. Here it shares the field with the Blue Burgundy (Pinot noir de Bourgogne), failing however to match it for quality. For this last-named vine produces the very best red wine. This reputation has helped it across many boundaries, and for a long time it has been successfully cultivated in all the

*34 The "bearded grape" which grew at Albersweiler near Landau in 1542. Zentralbibliothek Zurich, Graphic Collection.*

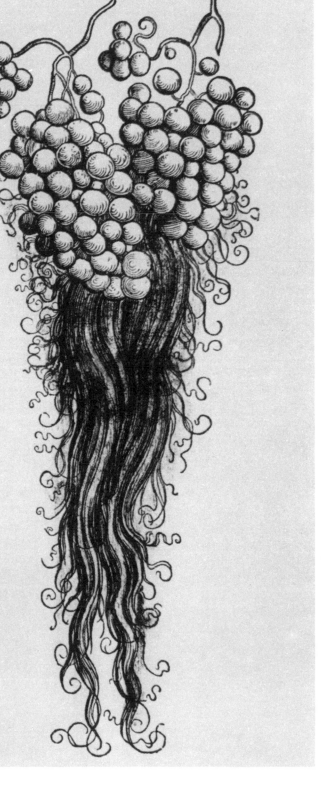

Ein warhafft wunderbarlich vor vnerhörte
figur vnnd gewächs So zů Aberoweiler bey
Landaw am Rhein im Jar der geburt
Christi M.D.XLI. zů Herbst
zeit erfonden worden.

Wen Trauben an eim reben aft
Zůsamen seind eing wachsen faft
Darauß ein rotter bart für trang
Sein leng ist einer spannen lang
Jn vnderft voneinander gatt
Johannsprung auß den steinlein hat
Munrau Tergols berlein nger
Gantz krefftigklich herauß getriben
Vnd alo des rebmans Weib jn sand
Verwundert sich lang vor jm stand
Auß fürwitz ettlich har auß ropfft
Zelet ft jn gar herauffer zopfft
Jedoch wid zum so g wachsen ist
On sondern trug vnd argen list
Do wards dem Churfurst angezeigt
Zů letft jm geschenckt vnd zů geeigt
Der jn zů Heydelberg noch hatt
Zill fürften Herren fehen latt
Auch ietz zů Speir vff dem reichs tag
Ward daruon gar ein groffe fag
Der Pfaltzgraff lies jn bringen dar
Trůg jn bein fürften hin vnd har
Deo sich mengklich verwundert hart
Das ein wein traub folt han ein bart
Vnd ein halm fünfftzehn ehern tragen
Auch thet man vom jungfräwlin sagen
Welchs lange zeit nichtz geffen hatt
Wie Gott ietz zeigt sein wunder thatt
On zweyfel schwer bedeutnus hatt.

Difer traub ift Römischer Königklicher
Maieftat zů Speir von Heinrich Vogts
herren Malern burger zů Straßburg wie
hie zů gegen warhafftig ab conterfeit.

1 5 4 2.

Mit Kayserlicher vnd Königklicher
Maieftat freyheit.

wine-growing districts of central Europe. In addition it has been introduced to the Crimea, Algeria, South Africa, California, Chile and Argentina.

Within its own country between the Gironde, the Garonne and the Atlantic coast it contends for supremacy with the Bordeaux vines. These include the varieties known as Cabernet-Sauvignon, Cabernet Franc, Merlot and Malbec. Grown for the most part unseparated, in "mixed plantations", they cover 80,000 hectares of French wine land. They give exquisite, full-bodied, velvety-red wines with a high alcohol content and a strong bouquet, whose quality improves with the years. The fact that their main growing region lies so close to the sea is not mere chance. From here the wines can be easily shipped out through Bordeaux. As early as the thirteenth and fourteenth centuries casks from Bordeaux were filling the cellars of the English nobility and the royal court in London. With them began the great age of French wine exporting.

In other lands the produce of Burgundy and Bordeaux vines has never quite reached the quality of the originals. In the Balkans and other parts of South-east Europe they have been replaced by varieties long known there, whose grapes often give growths which are fully comparable in terms of quality: Mavrud, Kadarka – known in Bulgaria as Gamza – and Pamid. As parts of a long-standing red wine culture, whose roots certainly go back to Antiquity, they all have a long history of cultivation. Their fruits are often mixed with each other after pressing. The result of such a blend of Mavrud and Pamid is the very popular Thrakia. Then there is the famous Egri Bikavér, or bull's blood, which as long ago as 1552 is said to have stiffened the sinews of István Dobo and his two thousand bold Hungarians in the successful defence of the fortress of Eger against an attack by a hundred thousand Turks. The basis of this wine is the Kadarka grape, which gets its name from the Albanian city of Shkodër (Scutari). Bull's blood is 70 per cent made up of this growth; the rest consists of 15–20 per cent Burgundy wine and 10–15 per cent Médoc Noir. This happy combination gives a deep red wine with rich aroma and bouquet. Despite its high acid content it preserves that velvet smoothness that brings it close to the great French wines.

The Burgundy grape is also highly prized in its light varieties, which are the results of mutation. The reddish-grey variety, known in German-speaking areas as the Ruländer, has its own special story. It was brought to the Rhine from Burgundy and Champagne in the seventeenth century, and planted initially around Speyer. But before this venture had really borne fruit, it was brought to ruin, and by French hands at that. For during the wars which laid the Palatinate waste over the turn of the seventeenth and eighteenth centuries the pillaging troops of Louis XIV dealt particularly savagely with its flourishing vineyards. Wine-growing in some places was almost completely wiped out. The newly-imported type shared the same fate. Only in extensively-ruined Speyer one plant survived, as if by a miracle. An enterprising merchant by the name of Ruland – or so the story goes – acquired the burnt-out premises where the vine had survived, recognized its worth and set to cultivating it. Selling cuttings from it was apparently the business of a lifetime. In the end he was selling shoots for not less than a thaler (a silver coin worth about 3 marks). From these cuttings sprang all the plantations of the grey Burgundy on German soil, and the name they carried from then on was Ruländer. Perhaps there is a grain of truth in the story. The grapes of the Ruländer give a mild, alcohol-rich wine with a fine aroma.

An ancient and noble wine grape is the red Traminer. There is something to suggest that it comes from the South Tyrol. We can establish its existence in Termeno in 1349, the year of the Black Death. Today it still produces highly-esteemed wine, in the Palatinate as well as on the Elbe. In terms of acreage, however, it comes second in both these German provinces to the Sylvaner, whose origins are probably to be sought in the Carpathian ridge. Its grapes in particular are responsible for the reputation enjoyed by the wines of Franconia. Goethe in his time appreciated them, and even when in Karlsbad was loath to do without them. He had a pail – some sixty litres – sent from Schweinfurt for his dining table, an amount which says something for his thirst. The poet himself confirms as much in a letter of March 24, 1820, reporting that along with the curative spring waters, he was drinking two litres of Franconian wine a day. He preferred it even when not taking the cure. Surviving accounts show that Würzburger, Wertheimer and Eschendorfer vintages were the mainstay of his cellar. He also took pleasure in the wines of Eger, Alsace, the Languedoc, Malaga and Champagne. But nothing we know about him suggests an appreciation of the Rhine Riesling. In this respect he shared the tastes of Schiller.

And yet in his day this most noble of all white wine grapes had already been known for at least three hundred years. In about 1490 it was one of the most widespread varieties in southern Germany. Towards the end of the sixteenth century it appeared on the Elbe, too, south of Wittenberg. It was probably developed in the first place from a seedling in the Palatinate or in the Rheingau, so·that the wild vines which still today grow here and there in the Upper Rhine valley may have had a part in its creation. It flourished best on the Mosel and Rhine – although only in the best conditions. For with the Riesling the ripening of the fruit occurs relatively late. If the weather is favourable it will give white wine of the highest quality. And if St. Peter is particularly kind to the wine-grower, he gives them the opportunity, for an *Auslese* – a wine made from late-gathered grapes, from which all unripe ones have been rejected – or perhaps even for a *Trockenbeeren-auslese* – made from grapes which are partially dried from standing so long on the vine. The must pressed from such grapes makes the best, and also the most expensive wines in the world.

Towards the end of the last century a Swiss researcher by the not particularly rare name of Müller, who came from the canton of Thurgau, was working in Geisenheim on the Rhine. He succeeded in persuading the Riesling to marry with the Sylvaner, producing a new sort of vine which was named Müller-Thurgau after its creator. It inherited several good qualities from its noble parents. In the course of further breeding it proved to be extraordinarily fruitful and of outstanding quality. To demonstrate its abilities it does not demand especially good conditions. In addition it ripens early and is very resistant to frost. Small wonder then that in the course of this century it has conquered a great deal of territory. Friends of wine are not slow to appreciate its mild, flowery wines, which are low in acids.

The noble vines of central Europe are flanked to East and West by cousins of equal birth. Hungary gives us the produce of the yellow Furmint, which was probably, like the Riesling, produced from seeds. Next to it comes the Debrői Hárslevelü (Lime-leaf), so christened from the form of its leaves. Together with the yellow Muscatel these two sorts are responsible for the quality of Tokay. Whether Szamorodni, Aszú or Eszencia, Tokay's must always contains a mixture of their fruits. We saw the same thing in the case of Egri Bikavér and Bordeaux. Incidentally the wine from the region of Jerez de la Frontera, whose name was contorted by the English into Sherry, consists of a similar blend. Its quality comes from a harmonious mixture of Pedro-Ximénez, Palomina, Muscat and Malvasia grapes.

The great reputation of Hungarian wine is further served by the Badacsonyi Kéknyelu (Blue Stem), so called from the colour of its leaf stems, and the closely related Badacsonyi Szürkebarat (Grey Monk). Both give fiery, powerful drinks, which definitely go with a heavy meal; not for nothing are they known in their home land as roast wines. A migrant from modern Slovakia is the Morí Ezerjó, whose best-known region surrounds the commune of Mór in northern Transdanubia. Its greenish-yellow grapes give strong wines of excellent quality, high in alcohol, which are best appreciated by those who like their wines dry.

The great white wines of France are produced chiefly from the white Sémillon and the Sauvignon, both of which grow mainly in the south-west of the country. Recently they have both been adopted in Rumania and Hungary, too. In their home land the wines made from them are often mixed with each other. Such blending demands all the artistry of the cellar-master. The results it can give are shown by the wines of the Château Yquem in the Sauterne region. The French designate them *grand premier crû* (first great growth), and count them among the noblest white wines in the world.

*35 Wine-grower with his tools. Catacomb painting. From: Fabretti,* Inscriptionum antiquarum quae in aedibus paternis conservantur explicatio, *Rome 1699.*

45

But where would coopers be, however skilful in their craft, without the skill of those people who plant, prune and bring the vine to ripeness: the wine-growers. They form a profession with a peculiar status, standing mid-way between the farmer and the gardener, and combining the experience of both.

Their long lineage begins back with those men and women who thousands of years ago first took the vine into cultivation. Their inheritance was carried on by the temple and court farmers of the Near East. They could no longer freely dispose of the fruits of their labour and already had no rights at all over the ground and the earth which bore the vines. Under the Greeks and Romans peasants, husbandmen and slaves all shared in the work. Slaves were above all employed in the vineyards of latifundium owners. Columella's writings give us a horrifying picture of the hard lives lived by these *instrumenta vocales*, or "speaking tools". Productivity on many of these plantations was probably low, and the growing number of technical publications on farming could do little to remedy this. Slaves of course did not study them, because they could not read. And genuine interest in their work, to which they were driven by the threat of beatings, was hardly to be expected of them. But by their forced labour the basic skills of vine cultivation were handed down unbroken to later generations. The expansion during Antiquity of the area given over to wine-growing was not least due to their work.

New practical skills appear right into late Antiquity to have been propagated mainly from the Near East. The sources for Gaul and the region West of the Rhine often mention Syrian gardeners working in the service of the great villa owners. It must be remembered that "Syrian" was a very general term at this time, being applied to nearly everything from an area between Palestine and Armenia. The specialists from this region possessed old inherited skills in particular fields of agriculture, which they now transmitted to the western part of the Empire. It is certainly no accident that their appearance on a large scale coincides roughly with the development of the first Christian communes in Gaul and in Germania west of

the Rhine. Doubtless many of them were bearers and preachers of the new faith, which found its first defenders among the ranks of "small people", the underprivileged of the provinces, slaves and freedmen.

Gardeners and small husbandmen as well as slaves tied to the soil, the so-called *coloni*, preserved the essential skills of wine-growing through the dark and bloody period of the great migrations. They may have passed them on to the Frankish, Alemann and Bavarian peasants, who themselves declined into an increasingly inferior economic and social position, with the development of feudalism in the following centuries. But as vassals or serfs, however, they could also till their own vineyards, albeit laden with tithes, alongside the plantations of their temporal or ecclesiastical lords. Their interest in the vine's welfare was therefore greater than that of the slaves of Antiquity. At the same time they benefited from various new technical skills passed on to them by learned clerics. Between the twelfth and fourteenth centuries the Cistercian Order performed particularly good service in this field. Many a model vineyard between Burgundy and Pomerania was set up by its brothers, most of whom were by origin simple men.

From the eleventh and twelfth centuries the peasant was joined increasingly by the burgher as owner, though less frequently as tiller, of wine land. The townsman was not infrequently in a better initial position than his country cousin, for his land was generally less heavily taxed. In addition there was the rapid development of the wine trade, now filling the roads, rivers and seas of Europe far into the East with barrel-laden carts and cargo ships. The city merchants had great opportunities for considerable profits.

In all regions in any way suitable for the vine, craftsmen and tradesmen consequently began bolstering their income from the plying of their trade, by retailing their wines. Indeed, sometimes this source of income exceeded all others. Such a situation was reported in Dresden at the turn of the fifteenth and sixteenth centuries. In many places in France it may have been but little different. Romain Rolland's splendid Colas Breugnon, who comes from the same period, is depicted as an equally skilled master of the vine and of bakery.

*36 Fritz Rugenstein, "who was a wine-grower and day-labourer in the garden", died in 1508. The drawing, from the* Hausbuch der Mendelschen Zwölfbrüderstiftung *of Nuremberg, shows him gathering grapes with pail and cutting tool. Another curved knife for pruning the vines is carried as a symbol of his profession in his belt.*

Anno dni 1508 Jar ann sannt lorenntzi abet
zin der nacht do verschide prnder fritz virssein
der em wenngertner vnnd em tagloiner zin de
gertenn gewest ist vnnd lannge zeit pey dem
purckherrn vnnd zim pfarhoff zir sannt lorenntzi
gedienut hat vnnd em wunnderlicher scham
prnder gewest vnnd pey vi jar zin dissem
Annisenn vnnd der tob prnder gewest ich

47

This is also the period when the wine-growers' guilds grew up on the Rhine, Main and Neckar, on the model of the handworkers' guilds. As public corporations they joined in deciding the life of the community. During the Great German Peasant War they formed a revolutionary element which in some cases was not without influence on the politics of the towns. Possibly their rapid and stern reactions may have been prompted by the movement of wine prices. Following over-abundant harvests or a rise in imports, a fall in the price of wine could endanger thousands of city-farming livelihoods.

In a worse position still, were the day labourers who tilled the vineyards of landowners and wealthy townsmen. Some of them were treated as farmhands or domestic servants, while others worked on their own account, by contract. Their wages generally were insufficient to guarantee the minimum necessary for existence. When there was a family to feed as well, some additional toil was always necessary. These workers took to growing cereals or vegetables in the vineyard, often between the stakes, and occasionally undertook a modest amount of cattle farming. Landowners looked unfavourably on such market gardening on the part of their wine-growers. In many ways it had an unmistakably detrimental influence on the welfare of the vines. But generally they made no efforts themselves to improve wages.

Despite these negative aspects, wine-growing was still attracting more manpower. From Thuringia we know that in the first third of the sixteenth century large numbers of "hoers" from Mainfranken would journey every Spring to keep the vineyards of the burghers in good order. Their employment came to an end as a rule along with that of the wine-growers, just after the Autumn vintage. During the Winter months they had to fend for themselves. To the city authorities they were then often no more than a burden. Few cities in this situation demonstrated the same "consideration" as the council of Erfurt, which accorded its day labourers who were unemployed between Autumn and Spring, the right to beg!

A good many tears must have fallen among the vines. Magister Georg Horn, the pastor at Hammelburg in eastern Mainfranken at the end of the sixteenth century, was often a witness of

this hardship. In his "Account of Wine-growing", he chose words of deepest sympathy for the "poor workers, who with hoe, pick and mattock, on stony soil and rocks must so labour, that sometimes at night they know not where to rest their tired arms". If hard toil brings blessing, these men must have earned every right to it.

Since these "good old days" a great deal has changed for the better. Technical innovations have lightened the labour in the vineyard. They have made their effect particularly felt in socialist countries, through the large-scale production of farming co-operatives and state farming concerns.

Wine-growers remain as before – sturdy, skilled, and, when the occasion presents itself, cheerful folk. Today, as before, they are, as in the time of old Pastor Horn, blessed by toil. To understand that, one only has to help in a vineyard once, or look at the gnarled, crooked hands of the old men, hands that are a match for the hard, stubborn wood of the vine. Without these wise, hard-working men, without these sure hands, the march of the vine around the globe would have been impossible, and today not a single drop of wine would flow.

*37 Joshua and Caleb. Master Nikolaus of Verdun, 1181. Detail from the altar of St. Leopold in the Abbey of the Augustinian Canons at Klosterneuburg near Vienna.*

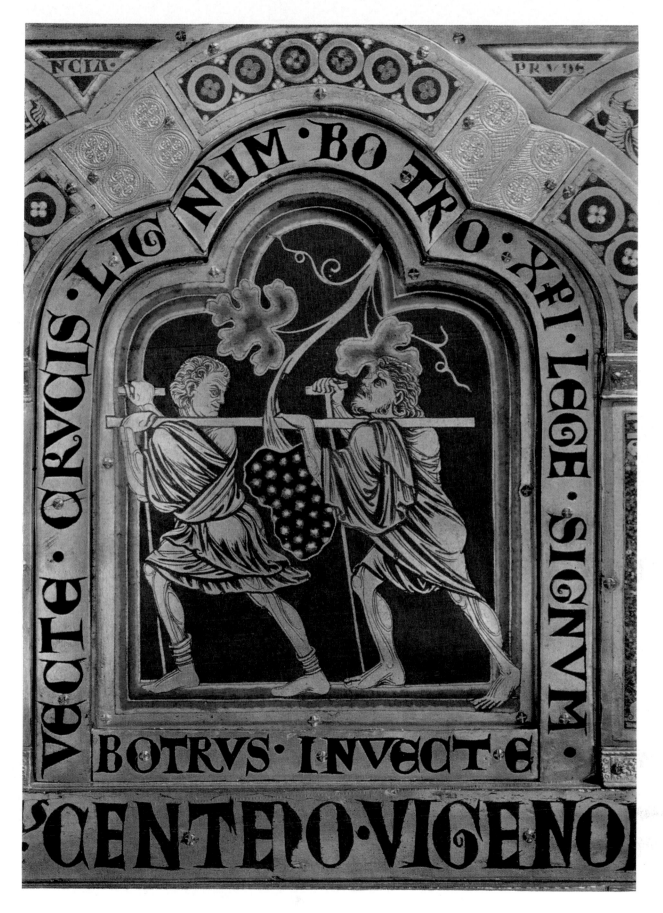

38 *The biblical emissaries. Grotesque figures by Jean Louis Gérardet, first quarter of the 18th century. Staatliche Kunstsammlungen Dresden, Grünes Gewölbe.*

39 *Joshua and Caleb. Guild emblem of the Frankfurt wine-growers.*

40 *Drunken Noah and his sons. Porch mosaic
from San Marco, Venice, c. 1250.*

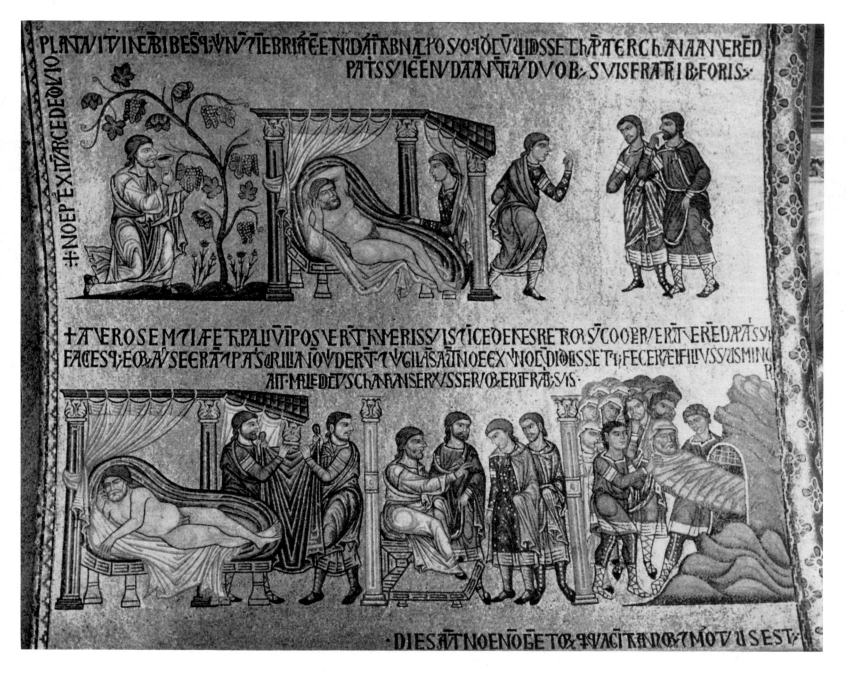

41 *Drunken Noah. Relief on the bronze door of Augsburg Cathedral, before 1065.*

42 *Noah, Shem and Ham. Group of figures from the Doge's Palace, Venice, 15th century.*

43 *Vintage, treading the grapes and storing the must in ancient Egypt. The method of training the vines is unusual: the vines grow in a double row, and the plants standing opposite each other are bound together at the top to make a low bower. The man at the jugs is possibly adding a spicing or stabilizing additive to the must.*
*Painting from the tomb of Kha-amwése, Thebes, 12th century B.C. British Museum, London.*

44 *Assyrian warriors with booty and prisoners from the city of Lakish in southern Palestine. Between the trees and bushes set along the road stand vines trained in a kind of Bockschnitt. Their branches are spreading without support like rays over the ground. Relief from the palace of King Sanherib in Nineveh, c. 700 B.C. British Museum, London.*

45 *The vintage as a symbol of Autumn between illustrations for Spring (Whitsun), Summer (harvest) and Winter (ploughing). From a copy made in 1028 of the Encyclopaedia of Hrabanus Maurus. Abbey of Montecassino.*

The Norman invading armies took their wine with them to England in 1066. "They draw a wagon with wine and weapons," explains the inscription on the Bayeux tapestry, which was made in the late 11th century. The conquerors thus held no hopes of any wines across the Channel comparing with those of their French homeland.

47 *Part of column from a Roman monument to Bacchus. The lower part of the relief shows a lad wielding a pruning knife with securis. Weinbaumuseum in the Historisches Museum der Pfalz, Speyer.*

48 *Amoretti working in the vineyard: pruning,*
*vintage, treading the grapes, decanting the must.*
*Gallo-romanic relief on a sarcophagus of Italian*
*marble, 2nd century.*
*Musée Archéologique, Narbonne.*

49 *Vineyards on the southern slope of the Troodos mountains, Cyprus.*

50 *Wine plantation in the vicinity of Tlemcen, Algeria.*

51 *Setting up a vineyard in Australia: planting the cuttings.*

52 *Vintage near Paarl, a centre of wine-growing in Cape Province, South Africa.*

54 Grape-picking machine in Californian wine country. It performs the work of fifty or more pickers. But its application demands a special support construction for the vines, which has the shape of a letter L stood on its head. The grapes hang down freely from the cross-piece. In this way it is possible to gather in passing about ninety per cent of the fruit, undamaged, by machine.

55 *The wine-grower. Painting by Ferdinand Hodler (1853–1918). Musée d'Art et d'Histoire, Geneva.*

# The Treasure in the Vineyard

### ☀ Ancient Praises of the Vine

"Every drop of wine costs a drop of sweat," says the vine worker. And with justice: although more and more machines of the most ingenious kind serve to lighten his work, there remains quite enough for hands to do. No machine can tackle the pruning of the vine, because pruning demands quite individual decisions. In any case, modern technology costs money, in wine-growing as elsewhere. Failing machines, failing co-operative assistance, the wine-grower is driven back, as in ancient times, to the hoe and the spade. Much of the wine still drunk today was grown with such techniques. The expert may be able to calculate for the wine-grower the number of hours of sunshine necessary for ripening. But how the heat, how rain, wind and cold afflict the man in the vineyard – that he usually forgets about.

It is true that the wages for his toil are high, at least in a good year. The vineyard can bring its industrious owner a cheering profit, higher than would a cornfield. But not every year is a good year.

Even in Antiquity wine-growing formed the most profitable branch of agriculture. Legislation aimed at protecting the vine was correspondingly severe. The Greeks set its malicious destruction alongside the crimes of temple robbery, treason and murder, for all of which the punishment was death. Thus enacted Solon and Drakon, the law-givers of Athens, at the turn of the seventh and sixth centuries B.C., serving well the interests of the vineyard proprietors, who made high profits from the trade in their produce.

No twist of historical fortune could affect the high esteem enjoyed by the vine. More than a thousand years later the tax regulations of the Byzantine state, which grew up on the soil of old Hellas, divided all arable land into two classes according to ground value. The first and foremost comprised all land on which vines grew. It was to pay eight times the tax levied on the second class of land, that was planted with ordinary farm produce. Such heavy taxation demands very high income.

There was a ceremony in Byzantium, on the 15th August of each year, which shows how keenly the great landowners, led by the ruling house and the Church, were concerned for the prosperity of the vine. On this day the emperor and the patriarch betook themselves to the vineyards outside the city, and there consecrated the ripening grapes with full liturgical procedure. All hoped to protect the vine from any encroaching evil.

More realistic measures were sanctioned by the *Lex Salica*, an early Frankish legal codex written at the beginning of the sixth century. It actually placed wine-growers under especial protection. He who took the life of a wine-grower was fined twice the sum payable for the same deed directed against a farmer. In other words, the French landlord could replace field hands more easily than skilled vine men.

German medieval law prescribed the same penalty for the malicious destruction of vines as for murder: the culprit's right hand was to be struck off. But pregnant women with an appetite for juicy grapes were treated with greater consideration in these olden times. They were to be allowed to eat as much as they could in the vineyard, and even take a grape with them. The respect for new life revealed in this law is particularly touching, considering that in all other matters the age proceeded strictly according to the Old Testament principle of an eye for an eye, a tooth for a tooth, a hand for a hand, a foot for a foot.

At this time the powers of heaven itself were also imagined to engage themselves in defence of the vine. The Palatinate legend of St. Cyriacus records what might befall the man who raised his hand against the vine. The cell of this godly man lay a long way from those abundant fields through which the famous Weinstrasse now runs. When he needed food and drink he had to tramp the long journey to Deidesheim. But every time that the hermit neared the city walls the gate flew open of its own accord to offer him hospitable entry, until one icy Winter's day the miracle failed.

The guilt lay with St. Cyriacus himself, for to help him on the snow-covered, slippery road he had thoughtlessly torn up a vine stake from a vineyard by which his path led, to use as a walking staff. The obliging welcome was no more. The gate failed to open. Rapid retribution, indeed, for such a thoughtless deed. This must have dawned on the transgressor himself after some consideration. The story recounts how he hurried back to the scene of the crime and drove the stake back into the ground. The return to Deidesheim must have been difficult enough in the gathering darkness. But lo and behold – the gate opened for him in the old way. The point had been made: the other man's vine was to be sacred, even for the godliest of men.

As European wine-growing during the fourteenth century neared its greatest extent, the value of wine land was sometimes set on a par with that of mining territory, as we see from a decree of Emperor Charles IV. The Emperor, noted for his wisdom in economic matters, formed the idea of making Bohemia into a land where orchards and vineyards contended for supremacy with the fruits of the field, after the model of Italy and Burgundy. To realize this ideal he took a concept from mining law – that ore-rich land must be exploited, on pain of confiscation – and applied it to vine land. Thus whoever now had land suitable for wine-growing and, despite warnings from the authorities, failed to plant vines on it, was to forfeit this land to someone more obedient to the imperial edict. It seems that Charles had very great success with this measure. Contemporary reports portray a Bohemia which for the abundance and fruitfulness of its vines fell only a

little short of the lands south of the Alps or on the Côte d'Or.

These efforts had only a short-term effect, however, because they came up against the nature of the land itself, and various other factors. Yet the temporary upsurge of wine-growing in central Europe left many traces behind it, which reflect even today its former significance. Not the least of these is the evidence of fine art – the vine, the vine leaf and the grape, as well as the toiling vineyard worker, became popular themes of both sacred and secular art.

Biblical concepts contributed to the development of these motifs. Wine-growers recalled, not without pride, that the man who with his family was the only survivor of the Flood, was also the first to practise their profession. "Noah was the first tiller of the soil. He planted a vineyard," these words we can read in the Bible, chapter 9 of the first book of Moses (Ill. 57). What happened next between the patriarch and his sons, together with its enduring consequences, has already attracted our attention. But from those first seedlings the vine twined through almost every book of the Old and New Testament. The vine and its fruits took on a symbolic value which was expressed in all manner of images. The most splendid is possibly that of Joshua and Caleb, who brought the grapes of promise to the people of Israel, wandering ceaselessly since their exodus from Egypt. They picked them in the valley of Eshkol. This region, even today, lends its name to a variety of grape – *nehel escol* – which produces fructifications (fruiting shoots) of over half a metre in length. The motif of the two messengers bringing with them the token of that promised land, which ran not only with milk and honey, but also with wine, has been taken up time and again by the pictorial arts (Ill. 37–39). The popular print has helped to ensure its living survival right down to the present day. Even now the couple with the giant grapes are never missing from any festive parades at the end of the vintage.

One of the psalms describes the people of Israel as a vine, brought from Egypt and planted in the Promised Land. The New Testament compares Mary's family tree, as well as Christ and his disciples, and finally the whole of the Christian fraternity, with the vine (Ill. 28).

56 *Wine-grower working in the vineyard. Behind the vines rises a watch-tower. Miniature from the* Codex Falkensteinensis, *11th century.*

In the multiplicity of its symbolism the Bible remains a rich source of evidence over early vine culture and the work of the wine-grower. There is a description of a vineyard in Isaiah which testifies to good observation and even expert knowledge. It lay in a fertile spot, was hedged around and protected with heaps of stones, and planted with choice vines. Its owner had equipped it with a watch tower, where in the ripening season a guard would have been posted. There was also a hollowed-out trough for the treading of the grapes. The description is so accurate that reading it one can imagine the whole estate laid out before one's eyes.

The painters and sculptors of the Egyptian Pharaohs left us masterly pictures of ancient eastern wine-growing. A tomb relief from the middle of the third millennium B.C., found in Saqqara, is one of the very oldest relics of vine culture anywhere. The fruit-bearing branches have been trained here into arboured passages. Similar pergolas, festooned with grapes, are brought to us most vividly in pictures from the grave of Nakht, a dignitary who served the Pharaohs in the fifteenth century B.C. (Ill. 110). Another painting shows the conjunction, typical for ancient Egypt, of horticulture with wine-growing. Thomas Mann in the second volume of his Joseph Trilogy, woven so strangely between legend and reality, takes us into this magic kingdom, well tended by slaves; Potiphar's garden is a palm grove hung with vines, a combination that gives double fruit – "paradisean, and pleasing to the eye".

The word of the poets is our only guide when we investigate the early stages of wine-growing among the Greek peoples. From long-lasting contacts with the peoples of western Asia they acquired, along with many other cultural goods, the secret of how to exploit the vine. Of all the fruits of this acquisition the transfiguration of wine into poetry must be one of the most precious. Ancient Greek lyric poetry praises the pleasure and stimulating effect of the noble

57 *Noah with his sons in the vineyard. Drawing for the 9th chapter of Genesis in the Velislav Bible, c. 1400. University Library, Prague.*

juice of the vine in a multitude of forms. The wisdom of the festive *symposia*, their profound conversations that helped the advance of knowledge, drew their strength from the moderate enjoyment of wine.

But poets were attracted not only by the effects of wine upon the heart and the senses. Several of the greatest, led by Homer and Hesiod, found the work of the vineyard itself fitting subject-matter for poetry. The student investigating the nature and character of their vine culture can gain a number of interesting clues from a reading of their verse. The Iliad, for example, gives us an original description of Greek wine-growing. Homer's descriptive account of the shield of Achilles tells of a vineyard artistically portrayed upon it by Hephaistos. Surrounded by fencing and a ditch stand the vines, tied to stakes. This is the first description of that new method of training vines, certainly specific to Greece, the value of which in the subsequent history of wine-growing has already been pointed out.

## ☀ *An Ass and Vine Pruning*

The pruning of the vine, another measure designed to improve its yield, can also look back on a long history. Possibly it spread around the countries of the Mediterranean during the Greek colonial period. The process of pruning, an apparently paradoxical measure – cutting back, so as to promote more intense growth, requires expert knowledge and precision.

The necessary knowledge must have been gained with difficulty, assisted, among other things, by the intervention of chance. A lively tale from Ancient Greece demonstrates how accident lent a helping hand. It began with a peculiar landmark at the harbour town of Nauplia, the port for Athens and not far from Mycenae. Here the visitor was formerly greeted by a relief in the high cliffs, showing a donkey in a vineyard. Many an intrigued traveller must have asked for the story behind this sculpture.

The townsfolk would have told him that a wine-grower betook himself early one winter morning with his donkey to the vineyard, to spread manure. He tethered his helper, who had pulled the dung-cart up the hill, on the thistle-covered ridge, where it could graze at leisure, while he set about his task within the vineyard. But the peg and rope could not have been fastened securely enough, and the creature soon managed to get itself free. Curiosity, and perhaps an appetite for something special, lured the donkey away from the prickly thistles. The leafless shoots of the vines gleamed temptingly, and their tart fragrance aroused his appetite. And so the little donkey began slowly but very thoroughly to rid its master's vineyard of as many as it could. The peasant was aghast when he saw the work of his four-legged helper, but the retribution exacted with his stick came too late, though doubtless it was heavy enough. In the end there was nothing to do but trudge home with his well-beaten donkey hanging its head. Meanwhile he contemplated the cut back in the coming harvest from his vineyard, already safely calculated in the annual budget.

So who could describe his astonishment the following Spring, when the vines put forth new, very sturdy shoots everywhere that the donkey had so placidly grazed on its wood – shoots, moreover, which proved to be quite outstandingly fruitful. Could this have been a hidden message from Dionysus, the lord of all vines, he wondered to himself, passed on to him by Dionysus's steed, the donkey? He knew that the gods could sometimes move in very mysterious ways to make their will known! The wine-grower decided to take the omen at face value, and in the following Autumn to follow the donkey's example with his own knife. The god of wine rewarded him for this care with copious fruit. And the grateful wine-growers of Nauplia, who all benefited from the newly-acquired knowledge, rewarded the four-legged emissary of Dionysus with the relief on the cliff face.

The progress of knowledge is here explained away by a light-hearted tale. And yet the real kernel of the story is easily understood, even if it was not Nauplia where the new knowledge was born. In the end it is not important where the cutting back of the vine was first practised. Since Antiquity it has been a basic part of wine-growing. Methods of pruning have developed in many directions in the course of time, and a distinguishing feature since Antiquity has been the type of knife used. In its many variations it is a kind of "leading fossil" – a key for following the paths by which vine culture travelled across the world.

There may often have been opposition to the introduction of pruning. Memories of such difficulties are preserved in a tale from the early history of Rome. In the hilly country around the eternal city the wine-growers at first refused to carry out this process, seemingly detrimental to growth. It required stern action on the part of the legendary King Numa Pompilius. To lend his edict sufficient strength he had to appeal to the highest authorities. Henceforth it was considered sacrilege in the Roman Empire to bring wine from unpruned vines to the altars of the gods. Of course, the pretensions of the gods happened to agree quite strikingly with the interests of landowners and wine merchants. The king himself, as a well-endowed member of the landed nobility, will not have been any exception. They all made splendid profits from the greater productivity which pruning made possible. Such a realization helped the innovation to overwhelming success. Without it the Mediterranean area and western Asia would never have become the hub and centre of wine-growing, and Italy would not have become Antiquity's wine land *par excellence*.

The Appenine peninsula achieved this eminence by an economic change which in its effects was double-edged. At the time of Numa Pompilius it was still, with the exception of the South, chiefly a land of farmers and herdsmen. About four hundred years later the elder Cato's pronouncement that of all forms of agriculture wine-growing is the most advantageous, signalled a tendency towards a basic change in farming. From being a land of cattle and wheat, Italy had become a land of the vine. The proprietors of the huge *latifundia* earned large sums from the export of their wine. But to meet the need for bread, corn now had to be imported.

## ☀ *Viticulture Promotes Wine Science*

This shift in gravity is responsible for many of our interesting insights into ancient wine-growing. For the interest of landowners in improving and raising their output prompted the appearance of a unique body of specialist literature, concerned with vine culture, as well as with many other branches of agriculture. Almost at a stroke everything about wine-growing, which up to this time could only be pieced together fragmentarily from pictures, legends and poetry, now emerges in precise text. But in compiling these books their authors nevertheless drew on many older surviving works, and found them most useful for their purposes. M. Terentius Varro, for example, one-time director of the library in Rome under Julius Caesar, reports in the introduction to his treatise on agriculture, that he has worked through, with great profit, the books of about fifty Greek agrarian writers. But of these doubtless highly informative books almost nothing has survived to our day. One of the few exceptions are the investigations into botany and plant physiology of Theophrastus, a pupil and friend of the great Aristotle. His discoveries, which in the sixteenth century were still con-

sidered the summit of scientific insight, were adapted to a certain extent by Roman writers for their practical use.

It is interesting to examine this circle of writers a little closer. The oldest of them was M. Porcius Cato (234–149 B.C.), famous in history as the implacable enemy of Carthage. This did not deter him, as a soberly-calculating landed proprietor, from studying on the spot the economic basic of this North African rival's prosperity, and initiating the translation of an agricultural textbook from the pen of the Carthaginian writer Mago. This source provided much of the material for his treatise *De agricultura*, a handbook which he wrote for his son and heirs.

The above-mentioned Varro (116–27 B.C.) was a scholar learned in many fields. Historian, antiquarian and philologist at the same time, his interests revolved above all around the practical exploitation of knowledge. We can see this from his three surviving books on agricul-

58  *Four types of vine training: entwined up a tree, on stakes, as a pergola and as* vinea camerata. *From: Vergil*, Georgica II, *Strasbourg 1502.*

ture, which in substance stand in descent from Cato.

These two native Romans were joined in the first century by the Iberian Iunius Moderatus Columella, who was born in Gades (modern Cádiz). In fact he wrote his twelve volumes *De re rustica* only after he had moved from his own wine-steeped shores to Italy. Wine-growing is reserved an extensive treatment in the text. Scholars of today still admire the splendid expertise of this ancient Spaniard, who produced from valuable literary sources, but also from his own observation, a classic work on ancient agriculture.

Outstandingly instructive information on wine-growing in Antiquity comes from Pliny the Younger (23–79), a Roman civil servant and officer. His *Naturalis Historia*, an encyclopaedia of ancient natural history, comprises 37 books. Continually quoted, though often less perfectly understood or consequently analyzed, are his minute accounts of the cultivation of the vine in the various provinces of the Roman Empire.

We can conclude this list of the experts of Antiquity with R. Taurus Aemilianus Palladius, a scholar who in a way also opens the chapter of those who lived upon the heritage of Antiquity. He was active in the fourth century. The fourteen books of his *Opus agriculturae* followed the course of the year and described the work of country folk from month to month, combining the knowledge of older authors with the writer's own experience.

This mixture, characteristic for all these authors, of direct reporting and literary tradition – and not infrequently of unproved superstition, to some extent thrown in as an exotic spice – allows us to reconstruct what is, in parts, a highly-detailed picture of Roman wine-growing, its tools and its techniques.

### ☀ The Training of Vines

It appears that all observers were particularly impressed by the very different forms in which vines were grown in the various provinces of the Empire. They immediately used these forms as a differentiating feature, being able to point to Herodotus for redoubtable support. Herodotus relates in the first book of his history how Ionian Greeks left Phocaea and after long travels settled down again in Oenotria. The name "Oenotria" can be translated roughly as "the land of the vine stakes". It lies in the South of the Appenine peninsula, at the tip of the Italian "boot". Herodotus's account probably confuses cause and effect, for we can assume that it was the Phocaeans themselves who first made southern Italy into the land of the vine stakes, just as they brought vine culture to the region around the mouth of the Rhône, with its centre of Massalia. Their method of cultivation was that of carefully ranked stakes which we know from Homer's description of the shield of Achilles. The Ionian settlers brought it with them to the western Mediterranean. Within antique times it was to make its way through the hands of Romans and Gauls northwards as far as the Palatinate, the Mosel and the Ahr.

In Italy itself other forms predominated. The Etruscans let the vines entwine themselves up trees. The same method is reported in Campania, the region around Naples. It has remained there unchanged, just as in parts of central Italy, for over two thousand years. The beauty which this combination brought to the southern landscape can be imagined from a painting by Jacob Philipp Hackert of 1784, showing the vintage in Sorrento (Ill. 60). The poplar, mulberry tree and elm are now, as then, the favourite companions for the vine. It is true that the partners to this union of plants, once celebrated by Horace, draw unequal advantage from it. For the vine, true to its original character as a climbing plant, snakes its way around the supporting tree, using it as a support and in turn being nothing but a burden to it. The Romans called this kind of vineyard *arbustum*, from their word *arbor* or tree. They thought very highly of it, for at least three vines could be trained up one trunk, and some wine-growers set its capacity at up to ten. A further advantage of this method of training was that it provided room for corn-growing. Broad strips of it grew between the vine-covered trees.

Neither the Romans nor the Etruscans can take the credit for having developed the basic elements of this form of intensive cultivation. The advantages of combining gardening with wine-growing were exploited even in ancient Egypt. Assyrian reliefs show that they had long been known to the wine-growers of western Asia, too (Ill. 24, 25). On the slopes of the Caucasus, as in certain regions of Italy, southern France and Spain, the method has survived right down to the present day.

Around the town of Brundisium (modern Brindisi) the vine stems were provided with yolk-like supports, whose horizontal parts were formed by a rope. The same method was also common in certain areas on the Iberian peninsula. But here however the field seems to have belonged to the so-called creeping vines; and according to Varro and Pliny the same was true of Asia Minor, Syria, Egypt and other parts of North Africa. They grew unmolested along the ground, and often without any props at all. We must not imagine that this certainly very archaic form of cultivation, also known as *provignage*, necessarily produced lower-quality wines. A convincing proof to the contrary is our modern Sherry. It comes from just such creeping vines, whose ripening grapes are raised from the earth by short props. More than any other method of cultivation this arrangement exploits the sun's warmth reflected from the soil, which is the reason why even today it is occasionally preferred in some southern regions. On Spanish soil it can be found in Jerez de la Frontera and in both Castiles. *Provignage* is also known in the eastern Mediterranean, on Crete, Rhodes, and a part of the Peloponnese. In the Middle Ages it was even used in many more northerly territories, such as Thuringia and Mecklenburg, although here it contributed to the ruin of wine-growing. The frequent and severe frosts caused far greater havoc with such plantations than in others where a higher form of training had been employed.

A reference from Pliny indicates the remarkable size to which the vine could spread. In the garden of the Empress Livia, he reported, a single plant rising like a tree had covered with its shady leaves the building of the baths, laid out under the open sky. The output of this huge plant he reckoned at twelve amphorae, which would be a good 315 litres of liquid. A note of his also reveals that the vine pergolas of Italy and southern Switzerland (Ill. 64–67) had ancient forerunners.

Pliny also gives one of the first precise comparisons of the different ways the vine was cultivated in the Roman Empire and its neighbouring lands. They are "of five kinds: either the branches lie in confusion upon the ground, or the vine stands erect of itself, or through a support without yolk, or the boots form a simple yolk, or four yolks are arranged shed-like". The "boots" here are the vertical posts of the yolk construction. Their horizontal part consisted of wood, hair, cane or hemp. To these five basic forms we can also add the trellis method (Ill. 63), the currency of which in ancient times is also proved by references in agrarian literature.

Thanks to their fitness for their purpose, these methods lasted for very long periods almost without change. Neither the devastating tidal wave of the great migrations, the collapse of the Roman Empire, or the assaults of Arabs and Turks could wash them into oblivion or fundamentally change them. They survived the horrors of the feudal wars. Since the sixteenth century they have had to prove their value in those places where the vine was a newcomer among cultivated plants: in South Africa, North and South America and Australia. Right up to the present day the picture of vines trained up stakes has

remained common to nearly all the wine countries of the earth. But particular growing regions have proved astonishingly obstinate in defence of other methods of training – a proof of the quality of these methods. The "shedlike" structures of Pliny have been preserved in the Palatinate technique known as *Kammertbau*, a word which goes back to the Latin designation – *vinea camerata* – for this kind of arrangement. Along the Weinstrasse, the use of the yolk construction – under the name *rehmenbau* – has also survived to the present; and the vertical support poles are still, as in Pliny's time, known by the name of "boots".

The technical innovations of the present day make use essentially of basic elements worked out in Antiquity. The so-called "high culture" system (Ill. 73), which allows the application of modern technology, with all its manifestations of mechanization, would be unthinkable without the ancient model of the yolk; just that by combining supporting concrete posts and lateral courses of wire they have significantly stabilized, extended and expanded it. The vine repays such thoughtful attention with a heavier yield.

*59 Hoeing and digging. From a Lower German translation of Aesop, Cologne 1489.*

In ancient times much consideration was given to the correct situation of the vineyard, and above all to the part of the sky upon which it looked. With plantations on hills the angle of the slope was also debated. But for this, as for all other criteria on which the flourishing of the vine depends, no generally-binding rules have been found. Modern textbooks prescribe minimum requirements, such as an annual sunshine record of at least 1,300 hours. Rainfall in central Europe over the same period must be 500–600 mm. (20–25 ins). In the South, because of the higher temperatures, this figure must be higher. From April to June, when the vine is growing most strongly, an average daily temperature of at least 12.5 °C (55 °F) is to be wished for. During flowering the temperature must reach 15 °C (59 °F), but higher would be better. The grapes then need 18.7 °C (66 °F) to ripen, and the wine-grower is well pleased if the sun gives more. These minimum requirements were only arrived at in the last century, on the basis of scientific observations. During the Middle Ages especially, at the time of the vine's greatest extent, the vine north of the Alps was on many occasions tried too hard. Encouraged by the expectation of improved income, people at that time trusted too heavily in the vine's not unjustly famed adaptability. Such experiments were doomed to failure. Some plantations were too far north, were too little exposed to the sun or were planted on heavy and cold soil. They could withstand neither fluctuations in climate nor developments in the economy. In every respect they brought miserable yields and were sooner or later given up in favour of more suitable sites.

More success was reserved for the attempt to find new slopes for the vine by setting up terraces. River valleys, in particular, attracted many such enterprises, on account of their favourable micro-climates. The result was worth the effort, as is proved by the sites on the Douro, on Lake Geneva and on the Rhine, all famous for the quality of their vintages (Ill. 61, 75–79).

## ☀ With Hoe, Mattock and Spade

The rhythm of work in the vineyard is perhaps described best, among all ancient sources, in Vergil's *Georgica*. It is in truth more of a hymn to the simple and "pure" world of the peasant than an agricultural handbook. In its pages, however, there speaks erudition united with close observation. It describes how the soil of the vineyard was broken up, three or four times with each returning year. The chief tool used for this was the mattock, a two-tined blade on a long wooden handle, which was used to break up the surface of the earth and turn it over.

Archeology provides us with further information about the tools used in the work. Finds of their metal parts demonstrate that in the tilling of the vineyard picks of varying shapes were adopted: with approximately round, oval or pointed blades. The spade was less frequently used, and the plough could only occasionally be brought to bear among the vines. Its use was hindered by the generally narrow spaces between the plants. These tools have survived in a wide number of forms right up to the most modern times. Their number has been enriched only by the adoption of the three-or-more-pronged fork.

One of Aesop's fables demonstrates very clearly, and with a shade of irony, what great importance was attached to the intensive working of the soil, even in ancient Greece. This version of the old tale is from a re-telling by the German poet Gottfried August Bürger:

"A farmer drawing close to death
Said to his sons with his last breath
'Our vineyard hides a treasure fair;
Dig ye therein!' – 'But father, where?'
Cried all around the peasant's bed
'Dig ye!' – Alas, the man was dead.
Now hardly was he laid to rest
They set to digging with a zest
With mattock, pick and spade and hoe
They dug the vineyard to and fro
And not a clod they left alone
But sieved and riddled every stone
And plied their picks both long and wide
O'er every inch from side to side.
And yet no treasure met their eyes
And each man thought the story lies.
Then hardly dawned the coming Spring
But all observed with wondering
That each vine bore a threefold prize

And only then the sons grew wise.
Then dug they, year and year about
The never-ending treasure out."

The discovery made in this remarkable fashion has remained right up to the present day the be all and end all of all proper wine-growing. All the specialist authors, all the prescriptions that have come down to us, name the repeated breaking of the soil as one of the basic conditions for success in wine-growing. It has its firm place in the wine-grower's treasury of proverbs. From Languedoc comes this truth from the time of Good King Henry:

"Once hacked – the wine smacks
The second time – good wine
Three times o'er – full butts sure."

The value of airing the topsoil before the blossoming of the vine is stressed by a verse from the Mosel and Rhine:

"Who over the flower the soil doth turn
Himself a hat and coat doth earn."

In representations of him in the fine arts the wine-grower's attributes are the mattock and hoe, and occasionally the spade. An early, unsophisticated piece of testimony comes from paintings in the Roman catacombs (Ill. 35). In the Middle Ages biblical symbolism found an important role for the toiler in the vineyard. This revaluation found its expression in book illustration as well as in church sculpture. The first printed books on wine-growing took up the motif and returned it to the worldly sphere of things.

*60 Vintage at Sorrento. The vines climb up around the trees and stretch in garlands from bough to bough. The picked grapes are trodden on the spot: in the left foreground the treading trough can be seen. A team of oxen stands ready to carry the must away. Painting by Jacob Philipp Hackert, c. 1784. Wallraf-Richartz-Museum, Cologne.*

61 *Vine terraces (so-called choirs) on the Mosel in late Autumn. Burg Metternich near Beilstein.*

62 *From tree to tree the branches stretch. Vine training in Umbria.*

63 *Working with vines trained upon trellises: planting the cuttings, bending and binding of the branches, vintage. A spade is being used for digging; its wooden blade is set with iron. Miniature from* Le Rusticon, *a French 15th-century manuscript. British Museum, London.*

64 *Vineyards of the Villa d'Este, Tivoli, in Winter. The covering slats of the pergolas spread across the landscape like filigree work.*

65 *Vine pergolas in the Verzasca Valley, Tessin.*

66 *Vine pergola in front of a wine-grower's house,*
*Quartino on the Langer See, Tessin.*

67 *New vine pergolas in ancient Pompeii.*

c xi kl' sci mathei apli euag.
f x kl' scoz. m. mauricij et socioz eius.
g viiij kl' sci lini. pp. qm.
A viij kl' scoz. m. cypriani et iustine.
b vij kl' scoz. m. cosme et damiani.
c vj kl' Dedicatio sci michael' archangli.
d v kl' sci ieronimi pbri.
e iiij kl'
f iij kl'
g ij kl'

From the second half of the fifteenth century there were several reprints of the *Ruralium commodorum libri XII* – twelve books on practical farming – of Petrus de Crescentiis, a mighty compilator of ancient agricultural knowledge, which had already widely fallen into oblivion. At the turn of the thirteenth and fourteenth centuries he himself ran an estate in upper Italy. The woodcut illustrations to his book include several representations of the wine-grower at work with his mattock. They also show the various ways of wielding the hoe, and perhaps two of its varieties. An allegory of Autumn, in which the season is portrayed as a handsome and sturdy woman vineyard worker, is attributed by art historians to the painter Francesco del Cossa, who was active in northern Italy around the middle of the fifteenth century (Ill. 80). Her attributes are the tools of the vineyard. Symbolic for the profession are the mattock, pick and spade, alongside the pruning knife, as shown on the eighteenth-century banqueting service of the Moravian wine-growers' guilds (Ill. 81, 82, 219).

These tools for working the soil have by no means disappeared even today. A comparison with other branches of farming rather emphasizes the stubbornness with which they have persisted, while in ordinary arable farming the hand tool, to a considerable extent, has already been driven out by mechanization. The reason for this discrepancy may be sought first and foremost in two characteristic features of wine-growing: the – on average – meagre size of holding, and the more or less steep slope upon which many plantations are built. Both these factors were for a long time an obstacle to the introduction of modern methods in working the soil.

Radical processes of land appropriation have provided one solution. Further assistance has come from busy workers and ingenious engineers. Nowadays there are many machines of different kinds for helping the wine-grower with the toilsome breaking-up and airing of the soil, even on steep slopes. But now men try to plant new vineyards on flat or only lightly-inclined terrain well-favoured by the sun. The advantages offered by the application of modern technology here are greater than any to be got from working on hillsides and terraces, even given

the introduction of ingenious tractor and soil-tilling machinery. The hard truth is that the wine-growing of the future will in many of its traditional areas gradually lose that power to shape the landscape whose aesthetic effects the fourth-century Roman poet Ausonius so intoxicatedly declaimed, in contemplation of the slopes of the Mosel:

"Leave other meadows, lend sooner to the eye the pomp of the vineyard.
Bacchus's gift may now afford a more beautiful spectacle:
Hillsides with vines in splendid array – how charming a vision.
Here where the ridge of the mountains in giddily staggering inclines
Ascends, buttresses, sun-topped heights and hollows and crevices
Girded with vines sweep up in a natural amphitheatre."

## ☀ *Gods, Heroes, and the Magic of Manure*

A process closely connected with the tilling of the soil is the enriching of the ground with fertilizing substances, so necessary for the flourishing of the vineyard. And yet the early sources manifest a measure of uncertainty over the materials and practice of manuring. The main reason for this may be that the effect of compost spreading was much more difficult to comprehend than the effect of manual working of the soil. Perhaps this is one of the reasons why the Romans elected to their already comprehensive pantheon of gods a patron spirit of manure by the name of Sterculus (Latin *stercus* = dung), and dedicated an altar to him in the capital city.

The mythological presentation of how manuring arose indicates the importance which was nevertheless attached to the practice. According to Pliny it was invented in Greece through the agency of King Augeas, whose stables, notoriously, fell somewhat short of modern dairy farming hygiene regulations. But Hercules, who purged this building for him, then carried the newly-acquired knowledge with him on his tireless wanderings to Italy – certainly one of the hero's more unsung deeds.

*68 Yolks arranged "shed-like" – vinea camerata – of Pliny's description pictured here in an Italian 15th century calendar. The grapes are being trodden in a perforated trough standing over the must barrel. Biblioteca Comunale, Forli.*

81

Even in Antiquity it had been found that the vine, despite its undemanding nature in comparison with corn, did not stomach certain types of manure at all, and made this known by a lowering of the quality of the fruit. Just as the particular properties of the soil can exert a specific influence on the flavour of the must and the wine, so the pungency of compost can produce very detrimental effects. Theophrastus, the ancient Greek, thus recommended careful choice of compost according to the type of soil. Some vineyards needed strong manure, others less pungent, and others only very light. Among the strongest he reckoned human excrement,

and then in order of pungency the dung of swine, goats, sheep, cows and finally horses, with – in his opinion the best – that of the donkey. Columella concurred with him on this last point, because the donkey's digestion is very slow, and therefore most thorough. In general he considered animal manure to be not particularly beneficial, as it spoiled the taste of the wine. He was much more in favour of bringing fresh soil and digging it in. This was more conducive to an abundant, better-quality crop.

In the Middle Ages and the following centuries there was no generally-agreed opinion on the substance and methods of manuring. Knowl-

edge won from observation and passed on was adulterated with some very odd-sounding ideas. As late as the eighteenth century recommended additives to stable manure were: refuse from the city tripe-shop, animal blood, and also yeast and the crushed remains of the grapes. The use of blood was not without certain magical associations, which through the belief in a mysterious sympathy between things, linked cause and effect in the most perverse way. Johannes Pauli in his collection of tales *Schimpf und Ernst*, written at the beginning of the very bibulous sixteenth century, used these beliefs in all-pervasive associations for his own moral ends.

Noah, he related, varying a legend from the Talmud, when planting the first vineyard dug four holes for the vine seedlings. In the first "he scattered ape's blood, in the second swine's blood, in the third sheep's blood, and in the last lion's blood; and the nature of these beasts do men take when drunk. The first are the monkeys, who caper and prattle, and should one of them break a rib in his body, he will not realize it until morning, when he is sober. Such are monkeys: whatsoever they see done, they also wish to do. The second are the swine. When they are drunken they feast and vomit and lie more under the bench than upon it, and lie in the dung, like other swine. The third are the lambs. When they are drunk they are most spiritual and tell tales, speak of Hell and bemoan their sins, even their drunken misery. They wish to reform the whole world, and in the morning remember nothing of it. The fourth are as lions, who wish to fight and stab and cleave, and will see the whole world dead. Let each man consider which he is most like." The truth of the fable can still be seen clearly enough, if we but study a sample of good drinkers.

In the last few centuries the considerable increase in the area of land given over to growing food in many countries has of necessity brought about changes in the means and methods of fertilizing. To the improvement of the soil by organic substances was joined the increasing use of minerals – a practical benefit drawn from steadily-deepening understanding of natural processes. Wine-growing, too, profited from such knowledge. Nowadays vine land is treated chiefly with potash, nitrogen and phosphoric acid, without having quite given up the use of manure. Additionally the wine-grower digs in peat, and of recent years for the same purpose, less important green plants such as lupine, broad beans, peas, mustard and vetch.

## ☀ Persistance and Change in the Wine-grower's Year

While the discoveries of science and technology both here and in other areas of agriculture have led to profound changes, they have made almost no impression at all on certain other work processes involved in wine-growing. The vine itself with all its stubbornness and the peculiarities of its growth has so far withstood all efforts to mechanize those processes by which it is given its wished-for shape. The bending, binding and pruning of the vine are today, as before, all done by hand, with the knife or with shears.

The cutting-back of the branches, the discovery in which the donkey apparently played such a remarkable part, is undertaken during the vine's winter sleep. In southern climates where frost occurs more rarely or is not severely felt, the pruning is counted among the tasks of Autumn. The colder North reserves it for late Winter. In Bulgaria it begins on February 14, the day of Trifon Saresan, according to a pious legend, a tailor who has been taken over by wine-growers as their patron saint. On this occasion the first cuts are sprinkled with good wine, in some magical way to encourage new shoots.

At first sight it seems paradoxical to cut back intentionally the growth of such an industrious plant as the vine – and the old wine-grower from Nauplia told his donkey what he thought about it with the hard end of his stick. And yet it does work. Along with the breaking up and fertilizing of the soil, it is precisely this pruning which helps the vine to give of its best.

Pruning, which right up to today has remained almost exclusively a manual task, reduces the number of shoots that grew in the old year, and thus confines the next year's fruiting to certain limited parts of the vine. Their buds – known as eyes – produce the shoots which will bear the coming grapes. With most methods of training the vine is bent more or less tightly into an arc or circle, into a heart shape, or alternatively into a roughly oval (horse's head) pattern. In this way the wine-grower equalizes the sap pressure to make for even growth of all the eyes – and thus attempts to increase the productivity of the vine.

Many forms of pruning still resemble astonishingly closely the processes which are described to us by the agrarian writers of the Ancient World. Two examples may make this clear.

In some provinces of Italy, Pliny wrote from his own observation, the vines stood "by themselves without any kind of support, through the

*69 Monks pruning the vines. Painted faience tile on a stove from the Summer refectory of Kloster Salem, Baden, 1733.*

drawing-together of their limbs and by short-ness promoting thickness." This description of the result of the pruning known as head-pruning (German: *Kopfschnitt*) could hardly be bettered for pithy conciseness. In such vines the fruit-bearing branches sprout from a short swollen stem squatting close above the root system. It reminds the modern observer rather of a pollarded willow without a trunk. The method is of value especially in regions which have hard winters, and has survived up to the present day in parts of Hungary, North-east Yugoslavia, Rumania, and Lower Austria, as well as in individual wine-growing districts of France, the German Democratic Republic and the Federal Republic of Germany.

A form of pruning related to head-pruning was already employed in Roman times, according to Pliny, and was probably known even earlier in North Africa and southern France. The vines were not allowed to grow "higher than the stakes. Thus they always look as if freshly planted, and stretch like craters equally across the fields." Nowadays vines treated in this way have a short trunk which thickens into a ball at the top. From this swelling sprout the short fruit-bearing stems. The upper part of the vine thus takes on a certain resemblance to the head and horns of a deer. This may have given the process its German name, *Bockschnitt*.

But Pliny did not know this expression. He compares the shape of the vine plant with that of the crater, a wide-mouthed mixing vessel for wine. The contradiction is easily solved. Speaking today of *Bockschnitt* we have in mind the bare, freshly-pruned plant at the beginning of the year. The craters of Pliny's description appear only later, when the fruit stems have achieved a certain length. Then the danger arises that the branches, if left unsupported, will bend down to the ground under their own weight and spread out over the soil. To prevent this the habit was, and still is, to bind the upper parts of the branches as closely together as possible. This process does indeed produce a vase-like shape from the curved stems and foliage, which can look perfectly similar to the ancient crater. This kind of vine arrangement could be found, and still exists today, in parts of southern Italy and Sicily, in France, Austria, Hungary, in north-eastern and western Yugoslavia, in indi-vidual districts of the G.D.R. and F.R.G., as well as in California (Ill. 53, 89, 90).

With numerous other variations of vine pruning a comparison can be made between the modern process and ancient descriptions which demonstrates the remarkable continuity of tradition. One might almost say that in these two thousand years of inherited skills more knowledge has been lost than has been added.

The fine arts also reflect in a certain way this persistance of tradition. Beside the peasant wielding his mattock or pick, wine-growing since Antiquity has been symbolized by the figure of the vine-pruner with his knife. In a Roman relief sculpture we see him amid a tangle of vines (Ill. 47). Late medieval book illustrations also portray him at work, giving us welcome clues for improving our rather scanty knowledge about the regional variations of his pruning tool (Ill. 36, 70, 84).

Many different sources feed the stream of wine-growing traditions. Many of them begin in Antiquity. "If one now reads all other German and French books treating of wine-growing, one finds that the basis of all of them are Roman prescriptions." Thus concluded in 1765 Heinrich August Fischer in his *Oeconomische Abhandlung von gründlich bessern und einträglichern Weinbergbau* (*Economical Treatise on Basically Improved and more Fruitful Wine-growing*). We have seen evidence enough that this inherited knowledge was not a flotsam of worn-out old folklore, but rather played a vital role in keeping vine culture alive. It was passed on by literate clerics, later mainly by scholars and men of letters interested in the improving of agriculture, and not infrequently by keen-witted compilers of almanacs. Its keepers and practitioners were the wine-growers and peasants. They above all put into practice these skills that came down to them in writing or by word of mouth, changed them to suit the conditions where they lived, and enriched them with their own experience.

This continually fruitful interrelationship of theory and practice is the reason for the fact that right up till today, a system of vineyard work has been preserved which in its essential features, excepting the use of chemical insecticides, was already tried and tested by the time of the Roman Empire. Yet we should not forget that its efficiency in the last hundred years has been

70 *Pruning vines on stakes. From: Petrus de Crescentiis*, Opus ruralium commodorum libri XII, *Speyer 1493.*

enormously increased, thanks to improved mechanical soil-tilling implements, to new fertilizers, and to the continued development of vine training methods. It remains as essential as ever before to break up the vineyard several times in the course of the year. This turning over of the soil between the plants encourages their growth and destroys weeds. Fertilizing, especially in Autumn, is also connected with this process. The continuity of vine-tending skills which were observed in the case of particular forms of pruning can also be seen in other tasks such as the bending of the fruitbearing branches, the tying-up of the new stems to their supports, and the taking out of unwanted shoots and superfluous foliage.

Now almost abandoned, although well-remembered by many older vineyard workers, was the practice of pulling-up the stakes in Autumn and covering the vines laid on the ground with a layer of soil to protect them against frost. Today we put more faith in the vine's powers of resistance. In regions where cold is a problem, selection for breeding purposes is directed particularly towards strengthening this quality. So now we may see vines on wintery hillsides, their often strange outlines making unusual patterns against the snow-covered slopes.

Another process which has gone out of use is layering, a method of reproducing plants well-known to every gardener, by the partial burying of branches. The process was very completely described in Antiquity, and right up to the end of the last century was a popular way of rejuvenating the vineyard. It came to a sudden end with the outbreak of phylloxera. This catastrophe, however, revived a procedure which had been painstakingly described and advocated by Roman agriculturalists for the planting of new vineyards. It was called grafting and played a vital role in saving vine culture from total extinction.

## ☀ The Enemy in Many Shapes

The experts of Antiquity and the Middle Ages would doubtlessly have considered with the greatest apprehension a process which in our times can be observed in the vineyard several times each year. On such occasions it looks dangerous to set foot among the plants. Thick, coloured clouds billow through the vines, spread by men with gasmasks. Modern chemistry has encroached in force upon the territory of the wine-grower! Dug into the soil, its products improve output. Sprayed on to the plants, copper sulphate and phosphorous compounds protect the vine from pests and diseases.

An undesirable characteristic of the vine is that it attracts all kind of unwanted guests to itself like a magnet. Looking through the history of its cultivation, it is clear that one of the wine-grower's greatest concerns has been to provide rapid and effective defence against such intruders. Over the last hundred-and-fifty years even the born optimist has been driven near to despair by the positively unearthly increase in the number of insect and plant enemies. The effect of chemical counter-measures has often been promptly paralyzed by the adaptability of the pests.

The problem of uninvited guests in the vineyard is an old one. Ancient sculptures portray sweet-toothed grape thieves of both four-legged and winged varieties. Stag and hare, as well as the nowadays rare dormouse, all attacked the young shoots. Birds preferred the grapes. That has not changed with the years. More recent accounts are quite specific. In 1730 Julius Bernhard von Rohr wrote in his *Viticultura Germaniae Oeconomica*: "Wild boars do unspeakable damage to the vineyard where they are allowed to break in. They not only eat the grapes, but trample the branches. When there are no beechnuts in the woods, as happened in 1724, as many as 16 or 20 go into the vineyards, and neither men nor dogs can keep them off the whole time. They are capable of eating up in one night one quarter, or even more on occasion. Foxes and badgers eat the grapes, as do stags, hares and other beasts."

Aesop told the tale of the fox in the vineyard and his fruitless exertions. Brock the badger is still a connoisseur of the fruits of the vine. Many wine-growers can tell quite amazing tales of his cleverness. It is said that badgers do not eat all their spoils at once. The finest of the berries they lay in a hidden part of the vineyard on a sun-warmed stone, and let them cook nicely through in the heat before enjoying them.

Sweet-toothed, four-legged visitors could be partly deterred by fences and walls. But these were only permitted on the lord's vineyard, while all peasant land had to stand open, in the interests of the feudal boar hunt. Against winged grape thieves no such defences availed. They called for rattles and mortars, if not for good lead shot, none of which helped for more than a short time. Today's wine-grower could tell you the same sad story. Starlings are the most feared because of the huge, sky-darkening flocks in which they can swoop on the ripening plants. If they are left in peace then the grower can save himself the trouble of picking! In ones and twos come blackbirds, thrushes, magpies, crows, pigeons, partridges and other "wine-greedy fowl", as they were called in the *Sächsische Land- und Hauswirtschaftsbuch* (Saxon book of domestic and farming economy), published in 1704.

Up to most recent times the wine-grower was almost helpless against insects nesting in the vineyard. Wasps and hornets were found particularly unpleasant. "They suck out the sweet grapes," complained the previously quoted Julius Bernhard von Rohr, recommending that one should "attack them at night with a sack and seize them." One cannot help wondering if he ever tried this himself!

Less dangerous for men, but no less destructive for the vines, were the invasions of beetles, which appeared at almost regular intervals. "In 1613, in May and June, was a large number of beetles, which caused great injury to the wine; could hardly be ridded of them," reports a chronicle from Thuringia. In 1617 the evil event repeated itself. Wine and fruit at the beginning of May were afflicted by "countless many" beetles. Two hundred years earlier a similar plague had visited the vineyards of Burgundy. The damage must have been terrible, because the wine-growers for a long period of time could find no way of controlling the insects. The unequal struggle continued for over a hundred years. When all human effort proved in vain, the wine-growers tried to win divine assistance. A public religious procession was organized. At the same time each man was instructed to go to general confession and abstain from swearing. The clergy threatened the pest with punishment and excommunication should it refuse to desist. Alas, nothing helped, and the Satan's brood went on to destroy almost completely the vines on the Côte de Beaune.

Thanks to the help of modern chemistry such destructive invasions are nowadays generally no longer to be feared. Nevertheless, the army of winged and crawling parasites seems to have increased from century to century by several special detachments. Every wine-growing handbook lists a bewildering array of these pests. The vine borer *(Byctiscus betulae L.)* eats off buds and leaves, while the female lays bare the leaf stalks and curls the vine's leaves into rolls in which she lays her eggs. Clover-hay worm and sourworm, the larvae of a moth which for its part also has the ominous name of "Grape-curler" *(Clysia ambiguella Hbn.* and *Polychrosis botrana)* destroy buds and grapes. The caterpillars of the pin worm *(Sparganothis pilleriana)* feed on the tips of shoots, buds and leaves. Accomplices in such pillaging are weevils *(Curculionidae)*, the red spider *(Epitetranychus althaeae* v. *Hanst)*, and various mites *(Eriophyes vitis Pgst., Epitrimerus vitis Nal., Phyllocoptes vitis Nal., Phyllocoptus viticolus Pant.)*. These evildoers are fought with various chemicals which are sprayed, powdered, dusted on or distributed in gas form.

The wine-grower is also pleased to accept natural help, provided in particular by several birds who can frequently be found nesting in vineyards. These include the robin, the hedge-sparrow and various types of titmouse. Not for nothing have these little warblers enjoyed special protection in old laws. Man was quick to recognize in them the industrious scourge of insect vermin in wood, field, vineyard and orchard. Sadly their numbers in vine country today have shrunk almost to nothing. Responsibility for this lies with the chemicals introduced to fight pests. Here is a case where man must, in his own interests, re-establish old and well-balanced relationships.

Even before progress in the natural science led to the discovery of the destructive power of particular mineral substances, men did not rely exclusively on the help of nature. Wine-growers worked to repel every insect attack promptly, by picking off caterpillars and beetles. To collect may-bugs all available hands were summoned, and even children were oc-casionally given holidays from school to help. At the same time men employed certain defensive measures which to our eyes seem rather odd. Caterpillars and louse would do the vine no harm, it was thought, if the pruning knife was smeared with stag's blood, or donkey or bear-grease. The same effect was attributed to oil in which these pests had been boiled. Garlic was also recommended as an additive. Such beliefs smack of medieval superstition, filled with ideas of magical protective charms.

Watchfulness, work and magic, were, it is true, equally at a loss when in the mid-nineteenth century occurred the threefold catastrophe which subsequently went near to wiping out wine-growing in large areas of the world.

It began with the powdery mildew *(Oidium)*, a fungus disease familiar to wine-growers since early times, and known in fact simply as "the grape sickness". Several times during the second half of the eighteenth century it caused extensive damage in Europe. Its fresh introduction with vines imported from North America had an overwhelming effect. This mildew from the New World spread with the force of a plague. Soon came reports of its appearance in Spain and Italy. In Germany it reared its head first in Swabia and the Palatinate. In 1851 the area of the infection widened to southern France, and Algeria, as well as to Switzerland, the neighbouring Tyrol, Hungary, Greece, Asia Minor and Syria. Ancient wine-growing districts were suddenly faced with ruin. In France, output between 1850 and 1854 fell by more than 75 per cent. Rescue came literally at the eleventh hour, even though the effect of the saving measure – the spreading of finely-ground sulphur, which destroyed the parasites – had been known since 1793.

The two other blows fell almost simultaneously, having a causal relationship. Vine plants from the New England states, and later from the river area of the Mississippi and Missouri, had been imported in huge quantities in the hope that they would be particularly resistant to the mildew. With them the vine-louse *(Phylloxera vitifoliae)* arrived in Europe. This scourge of wine-growing began its work of destruction around 1860 in southern France. In quick succession the alarm was sounded in England, Portugal, Germany, Austria and Hungary, and also in California. Further invasions during the 1870's completed the general infestation of Europe's wine-growing regions as far as the Caucasus and beyond. Western Asia was not spared, neither was North Africa. In Kashmir a blossoming vine culture fell almost total victim to the destruction. Even China and Korea were not too far for the mortal enemy of the vine to reach. In 1884 it began to penetrate into the South African plantations. Not much later came reports of disaster from South and Central America. Already since the 1880's parts of Australia had been affected. In about 1890 New Zealand's wine industry met the same fate.

Wine-growers must have felt that the battle with the mildew had been but a modest overture, in comparison with that which they now faced. The tiny insects, hardly visible to the naked eye, wrought unceasing havoc over an ever-wider area. They directed their attack chiefly at the roots, boring into the vascular system and sucking out the cellular fluid. Whole colonies of the parasites formed on afflicted plants, spreading their attack to the leaves. The wine-growers quickly discovered that absolutely nothing they could do had any effect on the murderous invaders. There was no other choice but to dig out the diseased, withering vines and destroy the pests remaining in the ground with poison and fire – a gruesome auto-da-fé. The dismay increased when it was realized that the insect was spreading not only underground, from root to root, but that winged forms, arising in the course of a complex life cycle completed above and below ground, were carrying death to widely-removed vineyards. By the end of the century, wine-growing regions over the whole world were showing frightful losses. France alone, within fifteen years, lost about 600,000 hectares of wine land. The social consequences of this world-wide disaster have to date received sadly little attention. One can the more readily imagine their dimensions, when one considers that in Spain, in 1889, as a result of the phylloxera catastrophe, eleven thousand men directly or indirectly connected with wine-growing, emigrated to South America – doubtless in the most miserable conditions and without much hope for a better life there.

Salvation this time came not from a wonder mineral, but rather from that gift of doom itself which North America had unwittingly bestowed upon the world. Vinland the Good had really done its name no honour. Its vines, which nine hundred years before had been greeted by Leif and his companions as a sign of promise, were now sowing misfortune after misfortune. Yet they themselves were to be the source of rescue. Among them were some strains – properly wild vines – whose hard root systems withstood the boring of the parasites. The problem was how to utilize this property. Taking over the whole plant would have been pointless, since the quality of its fruit was a long way behind that which men for thousands of years had expected of the vine. So some thought of the old process of grafting, and after many trials they succeeded in making the American foundations – that is, the root system – support all the noble varieties of vine. This process is now the common property of all wine-growers and has enabled wine-growing to recover, albeit step by step, but with good success. Most countries now promote this grafting by law. The area of "true-rooted" plantations, which stand a prey to the vine-louse and form perpetual danger points, is shrinking everywhere.

Unfortunately the import of phylloxera-resistant plants from America presented wine-growing with yet another dangerous enemy. In 1878 in the South of France downy mildew (*Peronospora*) was first noticed on one of these imports. Subsequently wine-growers gave it the descriptive title of "leaf-fall disease", or simply, "the disease". Within a few years this new plague spread through the whole of Europe as far as the Russian and Turkish wine-growing regions. It is known and feared everywhere in the world where vines grow. Damp climates encourage the appearance of its characteristic fungus, which attacks all green parts of the plant. Dry weather discourages or extensively prevents it. The grapes and must of diseased plants are of inferior quality. Downy mildew has wrought very severe damage to wine-growing, which can be measured above all by the shrinking of the area of cultivation. Wine-growers have been forced to give up altogether in regions with high rainfall, where the disease finds favourable conditions. Combatting the fungus with spraying or dusting with copper sulphate

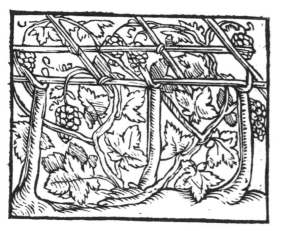

71 Vinea camerata. *From: Petrus de Crescentiis, De omnibus agriculturae libri XII, Basle 1548.*

and hydrated lime compounds has only been able to slow down the process. The disease still gives great trouble, despite the improvement of chemical counter-measures.

The steady increase in the number of insect and plant enemies is such that no remotely complete list of this evil legion can be given and has led to a considerable rise in the costs of wine-growing. It is reckoned that since the appearance of the vine louse the total costs of production have tripled.

Almost more fearful for the wine-grower than these pests are those natural events the effects of which he has so far been able to combat only to very limited extents: frost and hail. Both of them cause quite considerable damage. In the temperate zones, cold spells in the early part of the year can have overwhelming effects. Pankratius, Servatius and Bonifatius, lords of the days from May 12 to 14, are considered from old experience to be Ice Saints in the truest sense:

"Pancras, Servas and Boniface:
Freeze you to the marrow
And steal like a sparrow."

The wine-grower continually finds to his anger the truth of this saying, when he sees the damages wrought by frost. In unlucky years the "three lords Atius" are followed on May 15 by "cold Sophia", who finishes off those shoots that had managed to survive the grim trio. Means of defence are very limited. The best yet discovered is the method of smoking, which has been adopted since the beginning of the nineteenth century. By burning tar, crude oil, old car tyres, or any other strong smoke-producing material, a cover of warm smoke is spread above the threatened plantations before the onset of the frost. This minimizes the falling of the temperature as far as is possible.

Even in days gone by when planting out a vineyard men attempted to create a natural shield against frost. To prevent the swooping of cold air streams onto the vine-clad sides of river valleys, the natural vegetation of wood and shrub was left standing upon the topmost slopes. This wall of plants caught the first weight of the frost wave and prevented much serious damage in the vineyards below. Sadly such timber, which also provided material for the stakes, was later thoughtlessly sacrificed to short-sighted greed for profit. The damage resulting from this robber-farming is still felt by wine-growers in certain areas.

Defence against hail is a story in itself. In this field variations of a method which has in fact been known for a very long time are just beginning to prove themselves. For much of that time the idea of hail shooting has been derided by many. It was originally believed that the formation of hailstones could be prevented by shaking the air. The pealing of bells, to which were attributed magical beliefs with particularly great preventative powers, and also the detonation of small mortars, were used to achieve this effect. In some regions, such as Bohemia, wine-growers relied on the demon-repellent powers of the conch horn. Its hollow roaring note, or so they believed, would protect field and vineyard from storms.

Such miraculous physics does not really stand up to more sober judgement. Nevertheless, there was an idea in these activities which has been developed on scientific lines, in the Soviet Union in particular, to quite extraordinary effect. For hail shooting, according to the latest experience, does actually work. It is just a question of choosing the right ammunition. Special chemical substances have been developed which when discharged into threatening clouds by shells or rockets, cause the water particles to freeze instantly. This prevents the formation of larger hailstones. The small ice crystals melt back into water, into beneficial rain, before they reach the ground. In this way the discovery and influencing of natural processes turns a threat into a benign help.

72 *Wine plantation in a kind of* Kammertbau *at Acharnia on Crete.*

88

73 *Modern vine träining in the style developed by Lenz Moser. Plantation at Balatonboglar on the southern shore of Lake Balaton.*

74 *Above the confluence of the Bodrog and Theiss the vine-covered hill of Tokay rises to a height of over 500 metres. From its summit the visitor can look out far across the Great Hungarian Plain.*

75 *On these terraces the grapes for Port ripen.*
*Plantation in the vicinity of Vila Real, north of the*
*Douro, Portugal.*

76 *Typical vineyard landscape north of the Douro,*
*Portugal.*

79 *Terraces at the foot of Mount Etna, Sicily.*

80 *Wine-grower with grapes, pick and metal-sheathed spade as an allegory of Autumn. Painting, attributed to Francesco del Cossa, before 1470. Staatliche Museen, Stiftung Preussischer Kulturbesitz, Gemäldegalerie Berlin (West).*

81 *Rounded jug with wine-growing emblems*
*(pruning knife, mattock, grapes). Moravian faience,*
*18th century. Moravské Museum, Brno.*

82 *Wine-growing tools (hoe, pruning knife with*
*securis) and grapes on a Moravian faience plate,*
*1751. Moravské Museum, Brno.*

84 *Autumn work in the vineyard: hoeing and digging, pulling the stakes, pruning (knife with securis); vintage: cutting the grapes (simple curved knife), which are collected in a woven pail; carrying them to the treading vat in a hod with shield; treading and pressing (the front of the beam press is visible in the tower doorway); storing and tasting the wine. Miniature from Petrus de Crescentiis, Ruralium commodorum libri XII, Strasbourg 1486. The artist was probably the "Master of Margaret of York", 15th century. Bibliothèque de l'Arsenal, Paris.*

As yet the constant application of these and similar discoveries in wine-growing has not completely abolished the power of pre-scientific ways of thinking. The co-existence of the old and the new is particularly clearly visible where the protection of the vine is concerned. Even in our day the use of the most modern chemical products quite frequently goes hand in hand with corresponding intercessions to supernatural forces.

The Catholic panoply of Saints offers the services of a whole team of solicitors in the cause of the vine. Their legendary careers, their miracles or quite simply their names have given them their connection with wine-growing. Thus we have St. Vitus (Latin *vitis* = vine), St. Davinius (Latin *da vinum* = give wine), and St. Vincent, whose faintly vinous name was also felt to be a significant reference. Many of them administer very extensive areas.

French wine-growers generally direct their requests to St. Vincent and St. Urban. The latter also extended his dominion in the Middle Ages eastwards, into Franconia. Others, by contrast, such as St. Ingenuin in the South Tyrol and St. Otmar in parts of Switzerland, are responsible for relatively smaller areas of wine-growing.

Most Saints, however, owe their special position to the fact that their calendar days fall in those periods of the year which are in some way of particular importance for the work in the vineyard and its results. These dates are often linked with weather or growth forecasts, which reflect long experience in the studying of nature. Today they form an element of wine-growing tradition whose value science can frequently confirm.

The colourful procession, made up of members of many of the Old World's wine-growing countries, is led off by those Patron Saints commemorated at the end of January and the beginning of February. At this time, weather permitting, the vines are pruned. This is a job for which the wine-grower prefers good, clement weather. It not only makes the complex task easier, but gives a promise for the vintage. Such is the message of a proverb for St. Vincent's day (January 22):

"If Vincent's day do bring sunshine
There shall be good and plenty wine."

In Burgundy since time immemorial pruning has started on this same day. Also in this period comes the commemoration of St. Sebastian (January 20). Originally a protector against the plague, this Saint, in the faith of the wine-grower, has also preserved the vine against those myriad diseases which can afflict it. In the same month comes Charlemagne (January 28), who is particularly relied upon in the Palatinate. What else should we expect – did he not bring wine-growing in this region back to its former heights?

Candlemas (February 2), the day when, according to old beliefs, the power of Winter is broken, is the opening date for pruning in all German-speaking areas.

"Candlemas tide
Spinning aside
Sickle in hand
To the vine land."

Thus on the Mosel. In fact, they were not particularly anxious for blue skies on this date. This verse:

"If Candlemas brings storm and snow
Winter has not long to go,"

reflects rather the observation that the arrival of moisture-bearing airstreams at this time puts an end to Winter's cold anticyclones, even when this process is connected with very unsettled weather.

Until the most recent past in all the wine-growing countries of Europe, the end of that period in May, when the Ice Saints led their terrible cavalcade, was celebrated with great pageantry. Then on May 25 the feast day of the mild and clement St. Urban came around. He presents quite a story himself.

St. Urban differs from the other wine Saints by the odd fact alone that his figure north of the Alps was a fusion of two legendary characters: Pope Urban, the first head of the Church by this name, and Bishop Urban of Langres in France. The lives of both men were connected in religious tradition with wine. The first is said to have bequeathed his church silver vessels for the mass instead of the less costly ones usual at the time. The second was apparently hidden from his persecutors by a vine. It is possible to see in this miracle a continuation of the Dionysus cult in post-ancient times. In any case, St. Urban's day signalled to all vine workers the onset of warmer weeks. But its importance went beyond this cheerful fact. Much greater was its significance as a decisive date. "On St.Urban's day vineyards and orchards are earned," states the early thirteenth-century *Sachsenspiegel*, a legal code of great value. Thus the wine-grower, by conscientious work in the vineyard up to this date, guaranteed his rights to the harvest.

No wonder that the day was celebrated with festive gaiety and religious processions to pray for good weather. In the course of time they developed into rollicking celebrations, the centre point of which was the Saint himself or his mortal substitute. During the Nuremberg *Urbansreiten* which was practised up until 1621 in this free imperial city, a man was adorned in papal robes and before him in procession was carried a spruce tree hung with little mirrors and glasses. It is true that at the end of the march he was thrown into a water trough, but this in its origins was done with no malicious intent, being rather a watering in the spirit of ancient fertility magic. In the Swiss town of Sargans on the Rhine at this time they did the same thing with the same purpose, using the Saint's portrait instead. The custom was not without its vulgarized interpretations. If the weather on May 25 was bad, the angry wine-growers hurled St.Urban into a stream or even into the dirt of the street, as punishment. For:

"If the sun shines clear on St.Urban's day
There grows good wine, as people say
But if there be rain, it brings the vine
                                    scathe
And therefore St.Urban must go for a
                                    bathe."

Thus in Franconia.

In abundant Autumns, on the contrary, the Swabian growers carried his portrait down to the inn and draped it with vines. On the Neckar and Rhine the good Urban got as many bottles and glasses as there were drinkers around the table. In gratitude they annointed him with wine, and sang together in worshipful memory of the Saint the *Urbansminne* – actions which were also meant to favour future fertility in vineyards and gardens.

The Saint looked particularly severely on those who abused through excess his noble plant. He afflicted them with "St.Urban's plague", also known as gout. But he was at the same time appealed to as a healer of this disease, a quality which he shares with other patrons of wine-growers.

In the vineyard, within a short while of his feast day, St.Urban had to rely on the assistance of a whole series of further protecting spirits. For next came the flowering, which could be injured radically by cold or rain. At this same period wine-growers also feared the first great invasions of pests, with the massed appearance of clover-hay worm and fungus diseases, especially mildew and rust. Thus it is no surprise that among the Saints in the calendar for the first twenty days of June are several who, in traditional belief, share particular responsibility for the vine. St. Morandus is the first of them, on June 3. He acts as patron of wine-growers particularly in Austria and the South Tyrol. He is followed on the 8th by St. Medardus, who admittedly has a rather ambiguous relation to the vine. He is believed once to have ravaged a vineyard with a scythe when completely drunk! Nevertheless he is called on as a protector from rain during the flowering, although his reputation in forecasting makes him thoroughly unsuitable as a bearer of any such hopes. For:

"If Medardus be wet
It rains without let."

Wine-growers have said the same of St. Barnabas, who follows him closely in the calendar (June 11):

"If it rains on Barnabas
The vines will swim straight into the press."

With such weather the grapes will be watery, even if they do not rot completely. As heavy storms could be reckoned with at this time of year the Saint was also adopted as a guardian against hail. Even then hail shooting was not completely trusted.

Finally St. Vitus, one of the wine-growers' fourteen helpers, was meant to stand by them at this time. He had enormous responsibilities, not least as Patron Saint of the Holy Roman Empire. Emperor Charles IV had his remains transferred in 1355 to the Vitus Cathedral in Prague, then still under construction. At this time the Saint's day in the calendar (June 15) was still the date of the solstice. Possibly this position brought him his duties as a patron of agriculture, including the vine.

At the beginning of August, if the weather so far has been favourable, the ripening of the grapes begins. The wine-grower hopes for much sun both in this month and the next, so that the grapes can really bake through. The association with St. Laurence, who is thought to have suffered death on a red-hot grid iron, was readily made in older times. His day (August 10) fell in the middle of the hoped-for hot spell. If it was not sunny, men feared with justice for the quality of the ripening grapes:

"Be Laurence without fire
A chilly wine is all your hire."

The importance and consequence of good weather at this period is stressed by a wine-growing proverb about the Assumption of the Virgin Mary (August 15):

"Clear day and sunshine
Assumption day if it be fine
Proffers well for goodly wine."

This date has a very old connection with wine-growing. In the East it meant the beginning of the vintage, with all manner of ceremony. It was an occasion rich in allegorical associations. An inebriated victory procession, as also the death of Dionysus, symbolized by the path of the grapes from the vine to the wine press, formed the central theme of this extraordinarily popular feast, so eagerly celebrated by a large proportion of the people. Christian missionary efforts gave the feast a new content. An edict of the Byzantine Emperor Mauritius (588–602) proclaimed this day for an important event in the church calendar, the Assumption of the

Mother of God. The association with the vine was already given, as Mary in early Christian tradition was seen as the vine upon which the grape of Jesus grew. The Byzantine church father Johannes Damascenus, writing in about 700 explained her in these terms: "From the Holy Virgin we have received the grape of life. Her son, the grape of the true vine, was crushed in the press." Parallels with the ancient Dionysus myth are quite obvious here. They lead us deep into that religious upheaval and intermixture through which the Near East at this period was going. The feast of blessing the grapes was a synthesizing event. On Assumption day the emperor and the patriarch went out from Byzantium together. The idea of Mary the vine, the most perfect scion on the mystic stock of Christ's forebears, found expression in ecclesiastical fine art. Countless sculptures and paintings have taken the motif of the grape Madonna as their theme (Ill. 29). It is readily understandable that wine-growers should have chosen her as their supreme patroness.

Around the Assumption and St. Laurence are grouped several Saints who share with them in the protection of the vine. St. Sixtus is meant to promote the prosperity of grapes, as also of beans. On his name day (August 6) it was the custom in the late Middle Ages to bring the first ripe grapes to the church. St. Donatus (August 7) is recognized in Austria as protector of wine land against summer storms. Help against vine pests and diseases was expected of St. Rochus (August 16), who primarily dealt with the entreaties of plague victims. In this extension of his competence he accompanied St. Sebastian. The relation between wine-growing and St. Cyriacus (August 8) – whose misadventure in a vineyard we have already related – may be sought in his role as divine comforter to those afflicted by hard, servile labour. The forced vineyard labour exacted from tied peasants will have given more than sufficient reason for calling on him.

The last of the Summer's procession of wine Saints is St. Bartholomew. His day (August 24), remembered with horror by the Huguenots, is also significant for the weather, for:

"Bartholomew's day, howe'er it be
The whole of Autumn shall agree."

Or phrased negatively:

"Rain on Bartholomew
Bane on the grapes."

In the rearguard of these divine guardians of a good year comes St. Martin, warrior of mild deeds, bishop, and in the Middle Ages certainly the best-loved Saint in Europe, protector of the oppressed and scourge of all evil-doers. He was born in about 316 in Savaria (Szombethély Steinamanger), north of Lake Balaton, and was certainly familiar with the wine-growing of his Hungarian homeland. According to legend he brought wine-growing to the Loire, where in the neighbourhood of Tours he founded the cloister of Marmoutier. But more important than this deed for connecting him with wine-growing is the date of his feast day. In Antiquity November 11 was the feast of Aesculapius, the god of healing, when in his honour and with his purposes in mind the sick were administered with life-giving wine. The charity of good St. Martin accorded with this custom. The sculpture of the Bassenheim Horseman portrays him and the division of the cloak.

St. Martin's was also a decisive date, of hardly less importance than that of St. Urban – albeit with a negative accent. On November 11 peasants owing service or dues were summoned to hand over their tithes. The widely-celebrated Martinmas goose took its name from this. Formerly it roasted not in the pot of the farmer but went along with the must and young wine from his duty-laden vineyard into the kitchens and cellars of his feudal lord.

"Saint Martin boit le bon vin
Et laisse l'eau courre au moulin."

(St. Martin drinks good wine, and lets the water run to the mill.) Thus runs an ironical French proverb of the sixteenth century. The Reichsfreiherr vom und zum Stein took a blow at these hated exactions when, in an edict of October 9, 1807, he announced the long-overdue abolition of these oppressive feudal duties with the words "From Martinmas 1810 there shall be only free men." In fact it was to take much longer before the system was brought to an end. In itself it was contradictory and, for the farmers, thoroughly disadvantageous.

It was hoped that the weather on St. Martin's day would provide a clue to the coming year in the vineyard. Rain was wanted, as seen in this couplet:

"How many drops on St. Martin's on the
                                        fence
So many grapes next Autumn on the
                                        branch."
And:
"As the gutters on Martinmas run
So run in the coming year the presses."

A wine Saint who comes at the end of the year is concerned not with the work of the vineyard, but rather with the juice of the vine. On the feast of John the Apostle (December 27), who, according to tradition, drank a poisonous potion without harm, wine to which special powers are ascribed, is blessed in church. This wine is credited with sealing peace and love. It is also meant to revive the sick and give strength to those in the pangs of dying. There is a touching entry in the diary of Albrecht Dürer, writing about the final hours of his mother. She wished "before her death to drink the blessing of St. John, which she then did."

Many wine-growers on the Rhine and Mosel even today credit the "Johanniswein" with special powers in their own cellars. A drop in each barrel of the new year's wine is meant to lend it a particular excellence. The celebration of the first tasting begins with the call to drink "the love of John" – a custom which the Church has protected since early times. Through its influence such wassailing has carried over to the names of other Saints.

## ☀ Wine Land, Fine Land

Certain members of this large company of Saints can still be found today in some wine-growing regions. Their portraits, festively adorned on their name days, are at the same time an element of that aesthetic refinement that has distinguished vine culture since time immemorial from all other branches of farming life. Wine-growing over the thousands of years of its development has humanized the face of the land, in the very best sense of the word (Ill. 49, 50, 61, 64, 74, 76–79, 85, 88, 91, 93).

Wine country pleases us with the variety of its forms, all testifying to the creative influence of the wine-grower's work. His labour contributed and still contributes extraordinarily to the enrichment of our landscape. One of its results is terracing. Known to gardeners since earliest times, its adoption in vine country permitted the enclosure for cultivation of steeply-banked slopes in river valleys and on lake shores. The advantages of such arrangements have already been mentioned. Often terraced many times over, they stretch for miles at a time along the course of the Danube, Main, Neckar, Rhine, Ahr, Mosel and Rhone. The world-famous Port owes its quality largely to the effort of those wine-growers who transformed the deep-ly-cut valley of the Douro into an amphi-theatre of vines. Some of the very best Swiss wines grow along the sandstone terraces be-tween Lausanne and Vevey on Lake Geneva. In Hungary the growths from the north shore of Lake Balaton, where men's hands have pains-takingly sculpted the hillside, are put in the same top class (Ill. 94).

Even in those places where wine-growing has lost its previous significance, these stone steps not infrequently continue to testify to its landscaping powers. On the Elbe and the Saale orchards and fruit farms have now taken the place of vines on the ranked terraces. But the characteristic architecture of the vineyard re-mains, in a range which extends from modest grower's cottage to magnificent villa.

These buildings in and around vineyards are a constant feature of vine culture. Their origins lie in structures put up for particular purposes. Simple huts gave the growers shelter during bad weather. When the plantations were a long way from the village they kept their tools and even slept there during the busiest months. Characteristic for peasant wine-growing in parts of central Europe and in south-eastern Europe is the way these modest shelters were subsequently extended. The press was brought here, too. If the fermenting must and the wine were not stored immediately by the press a cellar passage was added onto these straw or reed-thatched, neatly whitewashed buildings. Many regions separated the press house and the storage place. Then the cellar passages lie at the edge of the district. Their coloured façades con-tain echoes of a modest farmer's baroque or classicism.

The lord's vineyard was characterized by an increasing concern with artistic excellence. Medieval miniatures give us an imposing pic-ture of such vineyard architecture, in which the vine sometimes seems to be no more than an accompaniment. But without its colours the buildings would remain lifeless. Today such a happy combination can still be felt in the vine-yards of Burgundy, the Gironde, Lake Geneva, and also at Castelli Romani (Ill. 64). While en joying this beauty we should not forget those whose labour in the vineyard first created the conditions for such a display of magnificence. Their unsung work generally goes unmen-tioned when art history takes off on a eulogy of this architecture.

It is also frequently forgotten what a lasting influence vine culture has sometimes exerted on particular areas of country life, especially in those places where, as in most of central Europe, it was the first specialized form of cul-tivation to develop to any size. Its practice de-manded skills for which the experience gained in ordinary farming was insufficient. The nec-essary new skills were propagated by properly educated agents – gardeners and wine-growers working in the service of the great landowners, as well as by the members of monasteries. But the skills they taught were passed on by a con-stantly growing number of peasants and towns-men. Only thus can the explosive increase in the extent of wine-growing during the Middle Ages be explained.

The new culture lent a specific accent to agri-culture, and enriched the practical knowledge of all who worked to propagate it. Later, when the area of vine land began to shrink, this fund of knowledge was to benefit the growing of fruit, vegetables and market crops, such as mad-der. It still makes itself felt today, even – or particularly – in places where wine-growing is almost no more than a historic memory. The work of the vineyard contributed in a wealth of ways to the development of our culture, creat-ing many things of value and leaving permanent traces behind it.

*85 Securitas and retinue in the vineyard country of Tuscany. Fresco from the cycle "The consequences of good and evil government" by Ambrogio Lorenzetti, painted between 1337 and 1340.*

SECURITAS

SENÇA PAVRA OGNVOM FRANCO CAMINI·
ELAVORANDO SEMINI CIASCVNO·
MENTRE CHE TAL COMVNO·
MANTERRA QVESTA DŌNA ĪSIGNORIA·
CHEL ALEVATA AREI OGNI BALIA·

86 *Palatinate vineyard house, Edenkoben on the Weinstrasse.*

87 *A grower's house in the Verzasca Valley, Tessin.*

88 *Castle Mělnik in the centre of the Bohemian wine-growing district of Czechoslovakia.*

91 *Vineyards of Cognac, Charente.*

92 *Vineyard gate at Clos de Vougeot, Côte d'Or, Burgundy.*

93 *View of the centre of Clos de Vougeot, once the greatest vineyard of Burgundy. It was founded by the Cistercians. Nowadays about fifty growers divide the ownership of its vines, which are still among the noblest on the Côte d'Or.*

# The Vintage

 *What Can the Year Bring?*

It is very pleasant to walk on a warm Autumn evening through ripening vineyards. Everywhere grapes peep from between the leaves: green, gold, red and deepest blue, surrounded by multitudes of insects, drawn there by the oozing sugary grape juice. At every step secret life starts into motion: birds flutter into the air, a mouse scurries away; here and there the vines creak and rustle – perhaps a badger, disturbed at its forbidden meal, is squeezing frightened into the surrounding bushes.

The wine-grower allows the guest to test the quality of the grapes himself. If these are real peasant vineyards that he is visiting such trials can develop into a whole vegetarian supper of crisp apples and juicy pears, and accompanied by a concerned dialogue about the prospects for the vintage, about memories of good and less good years. For all the wine-grower's thoughts are now fixed on the coming vintage, the weather, and those clues from which he tries to estimate the size and quality of the fruits of his labour.

The forecasts connected with particularly significant days have already been mentioned. At the heart of them lie observations of the connections between weather and growth. Taking them together we can see what exertions wine-growers expect of St. Peter.

He must start taking stock of their wishes very early, for "a good wine year takes two years." If the vintage in the following Autumn is to satisfy everybody, then the early Summer of the previous year must be warm and dry. Only then can the formation of buds take place which creates the right conditions for further good harvests. But if it rains in June or July during the flowering, not only the coming vin-

tage will be bad, but the plant will lose its fruitfulness for the space of several years.

Winter should be cold and dry. A mild rainy climate is dangerous for the vine, especially if it is repeatedly broken by icy spells. The programme for Spring sets varying demands. In March the sun must shine often to warm the soil through well and early. But the friendly weather must not last too long. From April and May the grower expects damp and coolness. They favour growth, but at the same time discourage the premature appearance of young shoots, which are vulnerable to the frosts common at this time of year. In June and July on the contrary the rain is not welcome. It hinders the fruiting or prevents it altogether. It also destroys the growth of the young shoots. Thus the wine-grower hopes for warm and relatively dry weather right up to the end of September, and even October. If he had the chance of artificially watering the vineyard in moderation he would be happy to do so. But wetness in the vineyard is very unwelcome during the ripening, for it lowers the quality of the must and encourages the onset of diseases.

The central European wine-grower hardly ever receives such favours at the hands of the climate. The changeability of the weather leaves him worrying about the outcome of his work right up to the day of the vintage. He looks with a trace of envy at growers in more southerly regions, whose grapes ripen under more favourable conditions. And yet it must not be too hot. The tropics are hostile to Dionysus's plant. It flourishes best between the 35th and 45th parallels, where the mean annual temperature is somewhere between 10° and 12 °C (59–64 °F).

But one should not imagine that the best wines grow only in the places where these requirements are continually fulfilled, as for example in the South of France. Nobody would dispute seriously the quality of a Muscat de Frontignan grown around Montpellier. The connoisseur would also praise in the same breath the qualities of more northerly growths, their elegant acidity, their sappy, flowery and fresh quality, in a word, their drinkability. Precisely these qualities emerge in the special climatic conditions of central Europe. The wine-grower gets them at the cost of considerable risk. In these latitudes experience has shown that a decade will produce only one outstanding vintage, two good and three of average quality. One will remain "small", and the remaining three downright miserable. This explains the maxim, repeatedly quoted in old textbooks, that the only proprietor of wine land who can face the future with any degree of complacency is the man who owns at least three vineyards, one behind the house, another in the cellar, the third, against all eventualities, in his purse. No wonder that the vine man over the course of the year has little feeling for levity. His celebration is the vintage – when it promises well, that is.

The wine-grower follows every stage of the ripening with attention. First the growth of the grapes ceases. Whereas so far they have been dark green, they now begin to take on a yellowy-green, golden-yellow, red or blue colour, each in accordance with its variety. The vineyard for the first time becomes bright with colour. Inside the grapes, meanwhile, a highly agreeable change takes place. From the sour berries of Summer they become juicier and sweeter from day to day. Their strong skin softens and thins with the process of colouring. Finally the passage of nutritious juices to the grapes dries up. Now they collect only sunshine, which helps them to form more sugar. Certain varieties at this time take on a brownish tone. "The fox has licked them," says the grower. Tiny droplets ooze through the tender skins. They lure all manner of sweet-toothed creatures: winged, four-legged, and not infrequently two-legged as well. Danger is nigh.

### Guards and Vintage Law

At this point up to a few decades ago a special state of law came into force in the vineyards, with the aim of keeping at bay all manner of uninvited guests. The vineyards were "closed", and thus separated off from the surrounding countryside. All paths which led directly to them were barred. The barrier might be a true turnpike, but a post inclined steeply across the path with a wisp of straw dangling on it was also sufficient. The initiated now knew that on these banned paths (Bannwege) there was no thoroughfare. From the day of the closure until the beginning of the vintage, a period of about a month and a half, no one except the authorized watchmen were allowed into the vineyards. The beginning and ending dates were fixed by the vintage committee, which the vineyard owners organized among themselves. In the Middle Ages this authority resided with the temporal or spiritual landlord.

The office of watchman was highly respected. A prime example of the breed was the South Tyrolean *Saltner*, whose title derived from the Latin term for a forester (*saltuarius*). His watchman's outfit, which also served to distinguish him from other mortals, included a leather jacket and a chain of brass wire around his shoulders on which hung a great many boar's teeth, a whistle and a blessed penny. On his head he wore a feathered hat, cocked into two points. This remarkable piece of headgear and mark of distinction demanded the contributions of half a company of hens, as well as pheasants and peacocks. On each side of this multi-coloured arrangement dangled handsome foxtails. In a high wind this ornament must have caused its wearer considerable problems keeping his balance.

His armoury included the cross-iron, originally a throwing weapon. It was considered a magical defence against evil spirits and witches. Nowadays the Sicilian wine-grower still attributes similar powers to the brushwood cross which he sets up at the edge of his vineyard (Ill. 103). The Saltner's arsenal was completed by a *Runggl*, a long-shafted curved knife with a square pike, and in certain regions by the halberd. In the vineyards around Bozen he carried a cavalry sabre. A symbol of office unique to the Lower Austrian vineyard watchmen should not be neglected here. They fastened to their huts, set up in the vineyards, artfully carved and joined, guardian stars (Ill. 102).

*95 This member of the mendicant order of friars in Nuremberg bore the very appropriate name of Niclas Pütner (cooper). As his portrait in the "House Book" of this order shows, he was by profession a maker of barrels. He made every kind of cask that the citizens of the town needed for the storing and processing of their wine.*

Der xxviij bruder der do starb hieß Niclas Wütner

The duties of the Saltner demonstrate what was formerly expected of a watchman in vine country. During his period of office he was not to leave the territory assigned to his care. He had to avoid public ways, and even confine his contacts with his fellow creatures to a minimum. The peasants in his patrol zone took turns to offer him hospitality, so that he wasted no time preparing his own meals. His whole attention was to be given to the guarding of the vines. He had to intercept grape thieves and show them off. And yet it was not a misdemeanor on his part to try a small taste himself. If a "poor man, a horsed journeyman or a woman in child should beg for a grape," then the Saltner should not refuse them. So say the old traditional Tyrolean codes. Alertness was enjoined against invading birds and other sweet-toothed creatures. Rattles, clappers and warning shots must all have helped here.

At the beginning of the vintage the watchmen took on new duties. In place of runggl and halberd their symbol of office now became the carved Saltner staff. Twice a day the Saltner was to sharpen the cutting knives of the vintagers. After the long time of solitary patrolling he returned to the merry chatter of the working day.

For the wine-growers themselves the preparations for the vintage begin with other duties. The hods, baskets, pails and tubs for collecting and mashing the grapes have been standing since the previous Autumn unused in sheds or in the cellar. Now with a rumble they are brought out and cleaned. If there is a river nearby which is still reasonably clean, all the apparatus is carted down there for an unceremonious bath.

The cooper at this time is very busy. Everybody is bringing him faulty barrels, and is anxious to have them mended and back the same day. At the same time he must have the barrels for holding the must in readiness. A cycle of figures from the Baptistery at Parma, sculpted in the second half of the thirteenth century, shows us one of these industrious masters (Ill. 99). Here in the yearly cycle he represents the month of August. Beside him representing September is a woman depicted cutting grapes (Ill. 98). At her feet is a skilfully woven basket.

The date of the vintage is determined by various factors. The first indication is the ripeness of the grapes. It differs in different latitudes and also varies widely between particular varieties. Gutedel and Müller-Thurgau are the first in central Europe. White Burgundy and Sylvaner allow themselves more time, and go to the press from eight to fourteen days later. In the rear come those varieties which need yet more strong sunshine in Autumn to come to full ripeness, such as Riesling and Traminer.

## On Spätlese, Auslese and Obliging Fungi

The observations of centuries, certainly stimulated and enriched by many an instance of chance, have led wine-growers to a further divison of their vintage. It brings us those precious wines which – springing from the best varieties of vine – come onto the market under the names *Spätlese, Beerenauslese* or *Trockenbeerenauslese*. Their creation demands a combination of favourable weather and good situation. Under such conditions the wine-grower can risk leaving a part of his grapes on the vine after the time of the main vintage. A week or two later, now overripe and rich in sugar, they are picked as *Spätlese* (late vintage). If the ripest of the grapes are picked separately the stage is set for one of the highly-coveted *Beerenauslese*. The crown and summit is reached if those grapes which have already shrivelled like raisins are taken on their own. Their rare and expensive result is turned out by the cellarman as *Trockenbeerenauslese* (dry grape vintage).

The creation of these golden wines also demands the assistance of a wind-borne guest from that consanguinity most unloved by wine-growers in all normal conditions: a tiny fungus called *Botrytis cinerea* which causes the so-called "noble rot" of the grapes. Its mycelium pierces the skin of the grapes into their centres and feeds on the organic acids still present, while leaving the sugar almost untouched. During this process the grapes shrivel, for their water evaporates. At the same time inside the grape the concentration takes place of those elements which are decisive for the quality of the must and subsequently the wine. The sugars and the flavouring elements form the bouquet.

*96 As an iron lock mounting the cellarman greets visitors at the door of the inn "Zum Schwan" at Salem, Baden.*

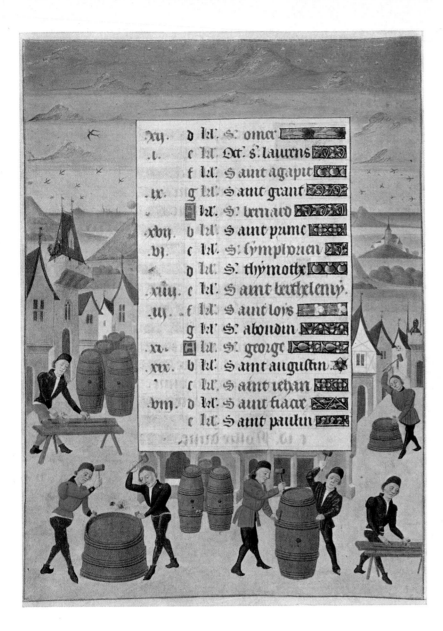

99 *The month of August: a cooper at work.*
*Sculpture from the Baptistery at Parma, Master*
*Benedetto Antelami, c. 1200*

97 *Making barrels: planing new staves, knocking*
*down the wooden hoops. Picture for the month of*
*August in the* Book of Hours of the Duchess
of Burgundy, *c. 1450. Musée Condé, Chantilly.*

98 *The month of September, represented by a*
*woman picking grapes. A beautifully woven basket*
*receives the picked fruit. Sculpture from the Cathe-*
*dral at Ferrara, 13th century.*

*100 Vintage. Tapestry from a workshop in the Loire region, 15th–16th century. The scene depicts the cutting and collecting of the grapes in baskets, their transport in a hod with a stepped rim to the treading vat, the treading and pressing of the grapes (small, very stylized beam press), and the decanting of the must into a fermentation vat. From their clothes many of the bystanders belong to the nobility: courtly society enjoys itself playing at "work in the vineyard". Musée de Cluny, Paris.*

*101 October vintage. Miniature from the Golfbook of Gerard Horenbout, early 16th century. Clearly visible is the hod with level rim, in which the figure appearing through the gateway is bringing the grapes to the screw press. In the right foreground the must is being decanted through a bowl-like funnel into fermentation vats. The vineyards rising behind the wall of the castle-like building are covered with vines trained on high stakes. British Museum, London.*

102 *"Long live wine"*, *proclaims this guardian*
*star, made in 1913. Weinbaumuseum, Krems.*

103 *This huge cross is meant to keep all evil away*
*from the vineyard. Vineyard at Gela, Sicily.*

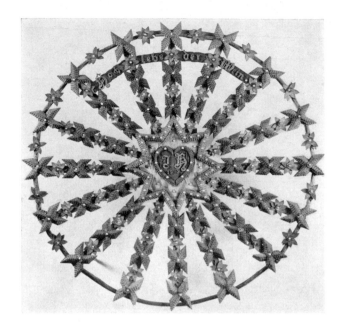

104 *Vintage at Sion (Sitten) in the Swiss canton of Valais. The onset of Winter, which often comes early at these altitudes, has covered the plants with a blanket of snow and frozen the grapes. This once highly unwelcome occurrence has been exploited over the last hundred years in the making of ice wine. The freezing of the water leads to the concentration in the grapes of sugars and flavouring substances. Ice-musts, in consequence, have a far greater sweetness and taste value. In terms of quantity they come far behind the juices obtained under normal harvesting conditions, but they easily make up for this by their highly prized quality.*

105 *The Ruländer has ripened well, too. The last days of the vintage on Lake Constance.*

106 *Californian wine-grower cutting grapes with a knife.*

107 *Vintage.*
*Miniature painting from the*
Leitmeritzer Kanzional,
*15th century.*

Without this process there would be no Sauternes and no Tokay. The natural circumstances which bring the grapes to such perfection are in part to be explained by the well-sheltered situation where the vine grows. The other factor is a quite special annual cycle of weather, which happily recurs by no means so rarely. Its many interdependent and mutually conditioning elements were excellently described 150 years ago by the Hungarian, Antal Szirmay, in a treatise on *The planting of the Tokay or Hegyalja vine)*. One can hope for a good Aszú – the equivalent of the *Trockenbeerenauslese* – "if the flowering time of the vine is finished by June 24, if in the course of July and the beginning of August rainfall prevents the scorching of the grapes during the dog days, if from mid-August to mid-October clear, dry weather predominates, guaranteeing an unrestricted, even ripening of the grapes and preventing the development of too high a moisture content. Neither rime nor frost must strike before the grapes finish ripening, for by withering of the stalks the circulation of the sap is restricted, and premature rough ripening puts an end to the ripening process before its full development. In mid-October there must be rain again, to soften the skins of the grapes, after which clear, warm days with cool nights and rosy dawns are needed to dry out the grapes, wither and shrink them."

Faced with such exacting details one cannot help thinking that the wine-growers of Tokay must long ago have concluded a special treaty with the divine weather authorities. Or perhaps they received such favourable climatic treatment for the way that, despite the misery of the Turkish times, when all warring factions took an equal hand in plundering the country, they remained true to the vine. Only – how did they come upon the secret of the noble rot in the first place?

There is a story on the subject which is not without parallels in the history of wine-growing. In about 1650 a martial Prince Rákóczi, at that time the ruler of Transylvania, put back the vintage on the Tokay estate of Oremus to late November, because of threatening enemy attacks. In so doing he unwittingly gave full rein to the course of events which is described so impressively by Szirmay in his abovementioned treatise.

Without wishing to question the truth of this tale, it does call for some additional comment. Basically it has been established that the knowledge underlying the *Spätlese* and *Beerenauslese* is as old as Antiquity. The Romans had probably learned it from the work of Mago, and practised it in the manufacture of their *vinum passum*, or raisin wine. Their process may have most resembled that by which nowadays straw wine is still produced. It involves spreading fully-ripened grapes on straw, or hanging them in well-aired rooms, to allow them to dry – a process which may take months. During this storage the grape juices are concentrated, and at the same time biochemical processes break down a part of the fruit's acids. The pressed fruit, under the name of dried *Beerenauslese*, can with good conscience compare itself with other quality wines.

The Romans very probably discovered a genuine *Spätlese* and *Auslese* too. Presumably such knowledge, along with other wine-growing skills, survived even the turbulent upheaval of the Dark Ages in the more stable centres of vine culture. But the system of feudal dependence, and in particular the system of dues which was an enduring and basic element of it, hindered the application of the process. The wine-growing peasant, bound to pay the tithe to his landlord, was obliged to think more about the quantity of his crop than of its quality. Experiments with any kind of late vintage were far from his mind, when he had to reckon on the chances of sudden rains or even frosts ruining his whole wine harvest. His tithe lords for much the same reason looked unfavourably on any such enterprises, and so their officials held the growers to an early vintage – too early.

Then, some time in the 1760's a messenger of the prince abbot of Fulda, charged with announcing the start of the vintage, was a week late on his ride to Johannisberg in the Rheingau. Once more, the story goes, men re-discovered and exploited the value of the over-ripe Riesling grapes. This admittedly sounds rather like the legend of Tokay. It is indisputable, however, that the introduction of the *Spätlese* in German wine-growing districts began in the Rheingau, possibly under the influence of the great experience of the administration at Schloss Johannisberg. The way was thus opened for improvements in quality, which could only make real progress after the final abolition of dues in the nineteenth century.

Since then the march out into the gardens and vineyards has shifted steadily forward towards the middle of Autumn. North of the Alps those times are past when grape-pickers could enjoy the warmth of the September sun on their backs. This is now the pleasure exclusively of growers in more southerly climes. On the Rhine, Mosel, and Saale men now set out in October – and in Tokay even in November – to plod between the ranks of vines, fingers stiff with the cold, and with knife or shears cut the grapes from the branches. But if the harvest is good spirits soon rise. The missing sunbeams are made up by a good draught of last year's home-grown produce.

At grape gathering the vineyards are alive with activity, more than at any other season. Every hand is useful, for a wet or frosty night, now, can destroy a great deal. None of the family is allowed to sit at home who can already, or still, use his legs. At mid-day the farmer's wife brings out a hot soup that both nourishes and warms the workers.

### 🦋 What Tubs Can Tell

From early dawn the picker's pails are filling. Medieval sculptures and symbols of the months show us the variety of their designs (Ill. 98, 100, 124). Until very recent times they have been made of pitch-coated basketwork or of wood. Their load goes into the hod, a container carried on the back which may hold from thirty to forty kilos of grapes (Ill. 100, 101, 107, 109, 141, 142). Carrying them is nowadays usually man's work and it is particularly arduous when the vineyard is built on steep steps. Formerly women were not spared either, as we are eloquently shown by the "hod people": little, richly-decorated works of art which were used as drinking cups in the guild rooms of south-west German and Swiss wine-growers. The high nobility boozed from them too, as certain very fine pieces from the seventeenth and eighteenth centuries testify. They can now be seen in the Grünes Gewölbe at Dresden (Ill. 125).

The shape of the old wooden hods allows us to infer something about the process of must-collecting and wine-making. Their numerous variations can be led back to two basic types. The first has a straight upper rim. As soon as such a hod was full the picked grapes were rammed down. During this operation the hods stood down on the ground. – After this first mashing the hods were shouldered and carried down to the presshouse with their contents. Hods of this type are found in regions where people produce mainly red wine, or where they in the past specialized in its production.

The second type has a steeped upper rim. An upswept side shields the head and neck of the carrier, who keeps the hod on his back while the pickers shake their pails, baskets and buckets into it. In this type of container, characteristic for the regions with a long tradition of white wine-making, the grapes are never crushed. The idea was rather to keep the grapes whole for as long as possible, and prevent too much of the colouring material in the skins from passing into the must.

But now we are on the way from the vineyard to the press. When the route was suitable the hods of grapes were emptied into bigger wooden containers standing on wagons or on wooden sleds. Now, as ever, they come in all manner of shapes and sizes: vats, barrels, tuns, huge troughs and baskets (Ill. 119). Here too the red and white wine districts formerly differed. In red wine areas these containers were designed for more lengthy storage of crushed fruit, and in consequence were generally very big. White wine areas, on the other hand, used smaller barrels and vats, in which the whole grapes were carried quickly to the treading place, to the press house or to the cellar.

Of all these various containers the tub enjoyed a cheerful metamorphosis in the Rhineland during the nineteenth century. The *Faschingnarren*, or Shrovetide carnival clowns, adopted it as the pulpit for their frivolous goings-on. From the *Bütt* in the days before Shrove Tuesday there poured forth a stream of doggerel and prose, song and speech, sense and nonsense over an audience grown up amid wine, and heartily amused by this temporary dignification of a wooden barrel.

*108 Cleaning the barrels. From: Petrus de Crescentiis*, Opus ruralium commodorum libri XII, *Speyer 1493.*

### Wine without Alcohol: Table Grapes and Sultanas

By no means all grapes give wine. This is true enough of real grapes, and not just of those offered from the *Bütt*, at Shrovetide. The real grapes, however, do not blow up, but serve a useful purpose. For even the teetotaller wants to have his share of the fruit of the vine. And not only teetotallers appreciate delicious table grapes, as figures can demonstrate. More than six million tons of grapes, that is more than a seventh of the world's annual harvest, is not pressed, but eaten fresh or dried. At the summit among producers of table-grapes stand Italy, Turkey, the Soviet Union and the United States. They divide more than half of the total proceeds.

The underlying reasons for this high demand are not all purely gastronomic. Historically the force of Islam has contributed strongly to the spread of this branch of vine culture. The Koran forbids the faithful the use of wine as a drink, but not in the form of grapes. So it is precisely in the areas dominated by Islam that the very best varieties of table grapes are to be found. Many new varieties have been bred by Moslems exclusively for this purpose, or for the extraction of sugar. But experts from other countries, which, with respect to wine grapes, count for little or nothing, have also made a remarkable name in this field. Who but the initiated, for example, would have guessed that Scottish and English greenhouse gardeners have taught Belgian and German growers how to rear new breeds of table grapes?

The other way of enjoying grapes without the intervention of pressing demands extensive dehydration. The result is our raisin, an essential ingredient in every good fruit-cake and without it whatever would become of the traditional Christmas cake!

*109 Hod-carrier mashing the grapes with a pestle. Picture for the month of September from a copy of the* Regimen sanitatis *of Heinrich von Laufenberg (1429), made in Alsace in about 1460. Stiftung Preussischer Kulturbesitz, Berlin (West).*

Raisins can only be produced where there is constant sunshine during the ripening period. Since ancient times western Asia and the Mediterranean region have been foremost in their production. The names of all the four main varieties – Smyrna raisins, sultanas, currants (from Corinth) and *Zibebe* point to this origin. The name of the last of these comes from the Arab word *zubiba* (raisin), which presumably during the Saracen occupation was taken over into Sicilian as *zibibbo*. From there it made its way with a particular variety of raisin into Austria and South Germany. During the last century new centres of raisin production have developed in the western hemisphere. The U.S.A. and Australia nowadays rank equally with Greece and Turkey. The Soviet Union, too, produces large quantities of these sweet dried grapes for the market.

Raisins are made in one of two ways. Either the stems are broken when the grapes are fully ripe and the fruit is left on the vine until the moisture in the grapes is completely evaporated, or the picked grapes are simply laid out on straw mats to dry in the sun, a method common in Spain. The drying process can be accelerated and the raisins given an extra shine by dipping them prior to dehydration in a lye of potash ($K_2CO_3$) mixed with a little olive oil.

## With Feet, Basketwork, Lever and Screw

This appetizing digression has taken us away from the grapes for the press, still waiting in tuns and tubs for their further processing. Nowadays this is generally a rapid process with which men have little more to do than supervise and control. Conveyor belts, cable hoists or large plastic tubes transport the fruit for mashing in the crusher-stemmer, a mill coupled with a machine for removing the stalks from the crushed grapes. If pressed along with the wine the stalks would spoil its flavour. When making white wine the grape mash is pressed without delay. With blue/black-coloured grapes for making red wine, on the other hand, the mash may ferment for several days or even a week or two before pressing. During this time of fermentation and the alcohol formed dissolves the colour from the grape skins, giving the wine its characteristic red tone, from rose to deepest purple.

Our modern presses are complicated machines. In them force is applied to the mash by the pressure of screws or rollers, hydraulic or pneumatic mechanisms (Ill. 146). Southern winegrowing regions often use the snake press, which works rather in the manner of the meat mincer well-known to every housewife.

Nearly all these machines were first built in this century. Their predecessors were the beam and screw presses. They may be written off today as primitive. But for about two thousand years men got some very fair wine from them. At all periods one could also find wines for which the must was won without any mechanical aid, by treading with the feet. The historical, cultural and ethnographic aspects of these old methods of expressing the juice, of their development and spreading, deserve our attention here.

Indisputably, the oldest method is treading. We have already referred to some of the archeological evidence for it – the treading troughs in Transcaucasia, Syria and Palestine, and the hollowed basins on the north-west coast of the

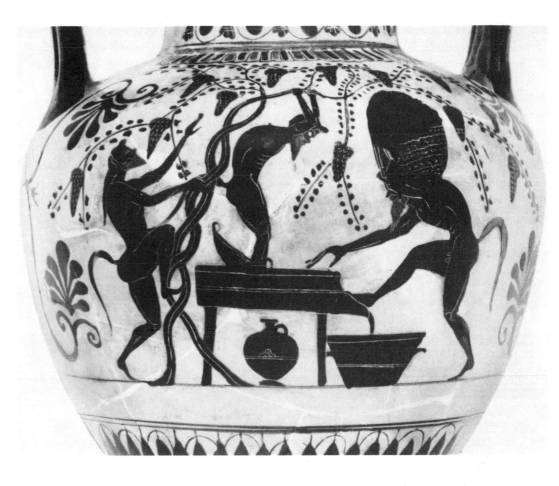

110 *Painting from the Tomb of Nakht, 15th century B.C.*
*Vintage and treading of the grapes. All the essential features of the must-extracting process can be readily understood: the walled trough, the arbour with ropes for the treading men to hold, the pipe for the juice to run off into the collecting basin, the fermentation jugs. The vines have been trained into a high bower. Valley of the Kings, Thebes.*

111 *Silens treading grapes in a trough of joined planks (in the style of the Bulgarian* korab). *Painting on an Attic amphora from c. 510 B.C. Martin-von-Wagner-Museum, University of Würzburg.*

112 *Silens treading grapes. The size of the basket in the raised trough is probably exaggerated. Amasis Amphora, second quarter of the 6th century B.C. Martin-von-Wagner-Museum, University of Würzburg.*

Black Sea. There is also the testimony of some very old pictures from Egypt from which we can make out the details of the process. One source of these is a tomb from the New Kingdom, the grave of Nakht, which we have already mentioned (Ill. 110). It is decorated with a wealth of paintings, among which winegrowing forms a central motif. One could almost describe it as a picture book of the early history of wine culture, so accurate are the details. The author of this work was doubtless a frequent and willing observer of the vintage. He shows how the grapes were broken, collected in baskets and carried to the press. It seems to be built of clay, and is roofed over by a trellis from which hang vines and ropes. Five men holding on to the ropes are trampling out the vintage with their feet. The juice gushes out through a pipe fitted in the side of the press, into a trough set below it. Further pictures show how it is filtered through a cloth before being poured into the tall fermentation vessels. Some more examples of these amphorae can also be seen in the painting illustrated.

All the details of the treading process are here explained. The only variations found are in the design of the press. In many instances it was let into the ground. The biblical parable of the untrodden vineyard describes the head of a family who planted a vineyard, built a fence around, and dug a press within it. Following the much older text in Isaiah this is a description of the model then current in the Near East for a grape-juice extracting installation. It would not have looked much different from the press around which Homer, in the eight-eenth song of the Iliad, assembles his vineyard folk:

"To this, one pathway gently winding
leads,
Where march a train with baskets on their
heads,
(Fair maids and blooming youths,) that
smiling bear
The purple product of the autumnal year.
To these a youth awakes the warbling
strings,
Whose tender lay the fate of Linus sings;
In measured dance behind him move the
train,
Tune soft the voice, and answer to the
strain."

In musical ringing tones the beat of the treading is evoked by the poetry. With singing and shouts they fixed the rhythm of the movement. Little of that has changed up to today.

The "lay of Linus", which is apparently closely bound up with the wine harvest, presents us with a certain puzzle. Greek legends tell two versions of the fate of this Linus. He was said to be the son of Apollo, and taught Hercules music. Once he admonished his pupil for a mistake, and paid for this with his life, for the hero abruptly struck him dead with his kithara, a stringed instrument. The example did not set a precedent – fortunately, or we would be short of music teachers. According to the second version he died at his father's own hand when he wished to compete with him in artistic contest.

The song of the tragic fate of Linus did not stand alone in the ancient eastern Mediterranean world. Herodotus reports in the second book of his history that the Egyptians knew a song by the same name, apparently very similar to the Greek Linus. In the language of the Pharaohs it was called *Maneros*. Not only was the song popular here. Herodotus records that it "is sung in Phoenicia, on Cyprus and elsewhere, and with every folk has another name." We may add what would have been to Herodotus self-evident; that everywhere where the Linus was intoned, it bore a relation to the harvest. His melancholy lament stood for the Autumn dying of a god of growing things, who brought all fruit to ripeness and with the end of Summer passed away. We do not know with which people the figure originated, although he seems to have an Oriental-Aegean stamp. Without doubt some of his characteristic features were later taken over by the Dionysus cult.

The state of pressing technology in the Greek heroic epoch can be deduced from excavations on Crete. Inside a building at the Mycenaean settlement of Palaikastro a grape-treading installation was discovered, the floor of which was lined with fine, hard mortar. It sloped in the direction of a large storage vessel. This pithos was let so deeply into the ground that its mouth stood level with the stone floor. During treading it was probably covered with a straining cloth or some sieve-like device, thus avoiding large-scale contamination of the juice running into it. Another press, still older but constructed on similar principles, was discovered during the excavation of a late Minoan farmhouse near Vathypetron (Ill. 143).

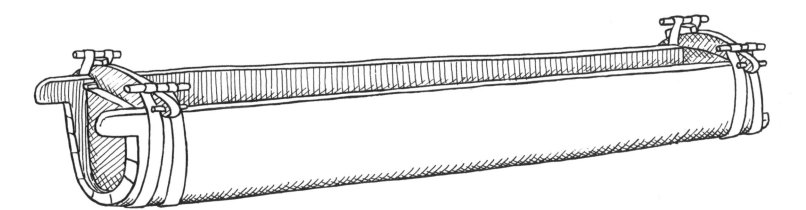

Roughly the same process lay at the heart of a wine "factory" set up by a Greek entrepreneur during the third century B.C. at Mirmeki in the Crimea, near the Strait of Kerch. At this time the region belonged to the Kingdom of the Bosporus. Here archeologists unearthed an installation made up of three treading troughs and two must cisterns. Their surfaces were sealed with a kind of cement. A further find was a shallow, circular limestone disc of almost one-and-a-half metre's diametre, with two concentric channels carved into its upper perimeter. Similar finds in neighbouring regions to the West, as well as in many Mediterranean countries, permit the conclusion that this was the floor of a treading trough. Its wooden walls were anchored into the inner ring. Around the outer channel the trodden juice ran into vessels placed to catch it, or perhaps along a wooden gutter straight into the must cistern. This installation, which according to the evidence was in use for about two hundred years, is not unique. In the forties and fifties another five of a similar type were found on the territory of the old Kingdom of the Bosporus.

Treading devices of this last type are similar to those which in south-east Europe today are known as *lin, korab, koruba* or similar. They consist of basketwork or of joined planks (Ill. 113, 115). The name *lin* can be traced back to the ancient Greek *lenos*, meaning a trough or bath. That containers of this kind were already in use for grape treading during ancient times is confirmed by scenes on Attic vases from the sixth century B.C. They allow us to understand some of the operation's characteristic features

(Ill. 111, 112). The wooden troughs stood on powerful supports and had a projecting runnel from which the trodden juice flowed into a large collecting vessel. The Amasis amphora shows us a pithos with most of its length sunk into the ground. Excavations in central Italy revealed the wider context of the arrangement pictured here. In these huge sunken vessels the must was fermented and the wine stored. Ordered in rows and by areas – to allow the easier recognition of varieties and years – these clay casks filled the interiors of farmhouses lying adjacent to the vineyards. Even today this picture is not wholly foreign to us. In Georgia a very similar method of preparing and storing wine has survived up to present times (Ill. 144, 145).

The vase pictures demonstrate that the grapes were not trodden directly on the floor of the trough, but that the treaders stood rather in a kind of basket, and the fluid ran away between the closely-worked fibres of it. The basketwork acted as a sieve, holding back pips and other bits of wood.

This method of extracting juice has been in use for over 2,500 years. At the beginning of our century it could still be observed in Georgia, parts of Bulgaria and Rumania, and even on the middle Oder. In central Greece it has even survived to the present. The trough consists of a large trunk which is carved out like a canoe, or is made of joined planks. Perhaps it was a feature of that old south-eastern vine culture which the Hungarians spread as far as the Carpathian basin in the ninth and tenth centuries, as they took over the land. Present

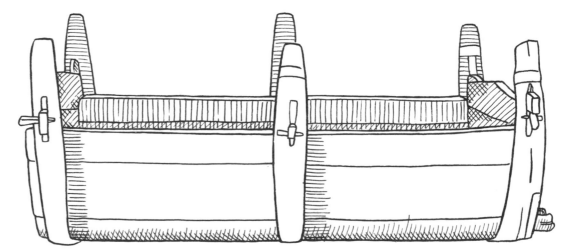

116 *Vintage and treading the grapes. Copy of a relief on the pulpit of the old Cathedral at Ferrara.*

knowledge has no explanation for its historical appearance on the Oder. For wine-growing came to this region in the twelfth and thirteenth centuries from the West, from Franconia. And here, with some exceptions, men used wooden barrel-shaped treading tubs.

The idea of drawing an older hereditary connection from the Black Sea to the Oder appeals to the imagination. But such a theory is not at present supported either by concrete remains pointing typologically in this direction, or by archival sources of any kind.

The ancient Greek name for the trough also raises a question. Does this *lenos* have any relation to the *linus*, the round of the harvest season? Philologists in fact are highly doubtful, so we must bow to their judgement, however attractive the idea of such a relation of language and sense.

Interestingly enough, another piece of grape-processing equipment betrays in its name an unambiguous connection with these earliest methods: the press, which in German is *Kelter*. Linguistic research recognizes this word as an early derivative of the Latin *calcatura*, a term used by the Romans to indicate a mechanical press. But the word's stem – *calx*, or heel – has older associations of a quite different sort. From it the Romans formed *calcare* or *calcitare*, meaning "to tread with the heel" – meaning grapes, of course. Thus the calcatura was originally a treading trough, dug into the ground or built up with walls, of the sort that Italian and provincial wine-growers used very widely. It differed little or not at all from the western Asian and North African pressing installations. But its name was transferred in the course of time to the mechanical press.

118 *Even the youngest lend a hand: vintage at Beaune, Côte d'Or.*

119 *Everything is ready for the new Champagne. Filled baskets of grapes in the vineyards of the Marne valley.*

120 *Harvesting table grapes in an agricultural co-operative east of Plovdiv, Bulgaria.*

121 *Vintage of table grapes in the Turkmen Soviet Republic.*

122 Vintage. The cut grapes are collected in woven baskets and carried to the press on a ladder-wagon pulled by oxen. This process allows us to recognize the making of white wine.

Book illustration from the Breviarium Grimani, Flemish work, probably by Simon Bening or Gerard Horenbout, before 1520. Biblioteca Nazionale, San Marco, Venice.

123 Late vintage in the vineyards of the Elbe. Painting by Paul Wilhelm, Radebeul near Dresden.

124 The month of September: cutting and collecting grapes in a small staved keg. Sculpture from the Baptistery at Parma by Master Benedetto Antelami, c. 1200.

125 Pair of hod-carriers from the beginning of the 18th century. Staatliche Kunstsammlungen Dresden, Grünes Gewölbe.

126 Hod-carrier in the style of the 17th century on the Weinbauer well at Zurich.

127 *This ancient relief tablet shows two grape treaders in a characteristic pose: with one hand they hold each other firm, so as not to fall over in the slippery mash. In the other hand they carry a stick with a crutch-like handle, which serves simultaneously as a support and as a tool for crushing the grapes. Museo Archeologico, Venice.*

In medieval Europe wine-growers still processed a not inconsiderable part of their grapes in the old traditional manner. Documents and acts, as well as numerous works of the fine arts, demonstrate how the treading process lived on unchanged through the centuries. In paintings, book illustrations and tapestries we see the barrel-like vat in which one or several people are trampling out the grapes (Ill. 60, 68, 116, 117, 127, 131, 140, 142). That they should without exception be men reflects not so much on the gruelling nature of the work as on a popular belief fed by certain observations, and quite as old as Pliny. He is quite convinced that women must be kept away from the press and the cellar, because in their presence the must and maturing wine will in certain circumstances spoil. Without questioning the truth of the matter here, it does seem that we can identify a close relevance to the narrow-minded behaviour of the ancient Roman patrician who chiefly kissed his wife when he wanted to discover whether she had been trying a drop or two in her lord and master's cellar! The punishments apparently were often dreadful. But then in the time of the Empire the ladies certainly held their own – even the most refined of them.

Many a fastidious palate may nowadays demur at the idea of the wine-grower stamping in a wooden vat. He can incidentally cite the fact that even Charlemagne must have had similar reservations, for in one of his edicts the Emperor actually commanded all wine-treaders to put on boots. In more than a thousand years many an authority has repeated his order, although in general without much success. In the museum of viniculture in Ehrenbreitstein near Coblenz, there stands a pair of large boots with thick wooden soles, which were in use during the nineteenth century. But booted treading was never at any time the general practice – neither on the Mosel or the Rhine, the hills of Hegyalja, the plains of Jerez de la Frontera, or in sunny California, as an old steel engraving quite unmistakably shows (Ill. 133).

But why was this so? Why did treading survive after the introduction of the mechanical press, with its far greater capacity for expressing the juice? And why did people tread even those grapes the mash of which was subsequently fed to the press?

The answer is simple. Trodden must was better than the juice which flowed from under the twisted screws and heavy beams of the wine-press. It was free of the tannin and bitter substances which pressed must inevitably acquired from squashed grape stalks and even crushed pips. It is true that the wine made from trodden must was in consequence rather shorter-lived. But every good cellarman knew ways of lengthening its life, and in any case it probably found its way to the table relatively young. Discriminating drinkers were extremely fond of it. Again and again we can read in yellowed archives the care that secular and church landlords, as well as the councils of the old wine-growing towns, took to see that trodden wine was barrelled separately. Almost every old textbook of wine-growing gives prescriptions for making it, storing it and lengthening its life.

Long ago it acquired a rival in the wine fermented from juice which dripped of its own free will from the grapes before they came to the press. Its name identifies it even in Antiquity. The Greeks called it *protropon*, and got it chiefly from Knidos and the island of Lesbos. The word and its meaning correspond to the German term *Vorlauf*, or "pre-run". The custom was – and still is, occasionally – to let this must ferment separately, for it had at least the same quality as trodden wine. A famous member of this family is the Tokay Eszencia. Anybody who has had a chance to sample it may consider himself favoured by Bacchus.

But there are few who ever aspire to this pleasure. Nowadays with some very small exceptions we drink wines whose must flowed from a mechanical press. Improvements in cellarage have ensured that they are in no way inferior to the great drinks of older times. Naturally they vary in just the same way with the character of the vintage, the variety, and the vineyard's location.

The techniques of their production were developed in Antiquity and in the Middle Ages. The Egyptians already had two different pressing devices. Tomb paintings from the Old Kingdom show their operation. The evidence of the pictures identifies one of them as similar to an apparatus still used by South American Indian tribes in the preparation of manioc flour, to press the unpalatable juice from the tubers.

They stuff the dough into a tube of woven plant fibres, called *tipití*, which when it is as full as possible they stretch lengthways. Its fibres are woven in such a way that the diameter decreases when it is stretched, and the resulting pressure expels the liquid.

The subjects of the Pharaohs appear to have used tipitís of considerable dimensions, the operation of which demanded not only strength but positively acrobatic agility. A picture from Thebes shows the device in action (Ill. 130). At each end stand two men, upright and kneeling, pulling at two poles which are stuck vertically through the ends of the pressing tube. Another has leapt between the upper ends of the posts and is pushing them apart as he hangs horizontally above the stretching fibre bag. How effective their efforts are can be seen from the dimensions of the vessel standing beneath the tube.

This method demanded a considerable amount of manpower, which only the proprietors of extensive estates could afford. These magnates, with their sizeable workforce, saw no necessity to develop more efficient apparatus. An innovation which allowed the more efficient use of labour did not appear until the time of the Middle Kingdom. Tomb paintings from the time of the eleventh and twelfth dynasties show that from about the beginning of the second millennium B.C. the torsion press was in use (Ill. 129). This contrivance involved stretching the sack-like container for the grapes across a standing frame. One end of it hung by a loop firmly from one post. The other was led through a hole in the opposite supporting post. Through its loop stuck the pole with which a group of workers wrung out the sack. The

number of labourers needed can hardly have been much fewer than for pressing with the tipití apparatus.

The Egyptians did not exploit the principle of the lever for pressing, even though in other fields they had used it to tremendous effect from earliest times. Its application to the processing of grapes was probably first attempted in the Aegean area. A process already known involved putting the trodden grapes into a sack or container and weighting them with a stone to drive out the remaining juice. Longus described the process in his idyll *Daphnis and Chloe*. In his time, in the third century, it may well have been considered outmoded. The method has survived here and there until our times, undergoing revival in peripheral wine-growing areas particularly when the harvest brings such little fruit that it is not worth employing the press.

The wine-growers of one of these marginal areas, lying on the Süsser See between Halle and Eisleben in the German Democratic Republic, have also preserved the knowledge of the oldest type of lever press. It consists of a heavy beam or trunk with its one end fixed in a hole in the wall. The free end is weighted down with stones or heavy wooden apparatus, and presses on the mash, shut in a sack, until the juice has run off. If the result is insufficiently satisfactory the pressure is increased by the addition of further weights.

Lever presses from the Mycenaean period, uncovered during excavations in the Cyclades, are almost identical to this primitive model – the only difference being that the fixed end of the beam was let not into a wall, but into a strong, vertically-standing post. However, this

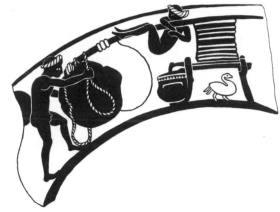

*128 Beam press for pressing wine and oil. Copy of a painting from a Greek vase of the 6th century B.C.*

*129 Ancient Egyptian torsion press. Copy of a painting from a rock tomb at Beni Hassan.*

*130 Ancient Egyptian press of the* tipití *variety. Copy of a tomb painting from Thebes.*

machine was originally applied not to the pressing of grapes, but to the extraction of oil from olives. But as early as ancient times it was adopted by wine-growers, too. A probable stimulus for its transference from the one field to the other was the growing demand for wine in Greek domestic and long-distance trade. It prompted the introduction of processes more effective than that represented by treading, with its great demands on labour and relatively meagre efficiency. The beam press represented the most up-to-date tool of the time. With it a team of four men could press in one day and 25 operations nearly 300 litres of oil or 2,500 litres of must.

But this does not mean that it was beyond improvement. Efforts were directed, above all, to increasing the obtainable leverage. This was achieved in various ways. One method was to increase the weight of stones at the free end, to the limit of the pressing beam's strength. Because of its capacity this type of press was later put to work mainly in small-scale production. In such conditions it has survived in places up to the present day in Hungary and Slovenia, and also on the margin of the wine-growing area of St. Pourçain in France.

A refinement of the pressing mechanism was achieved by the engineers of Antiquity when they installed under the free end of the lever a rope and windlass arrangement. With this aid the beam could be drawn down slowly during pressing. So enabling a more effective control of the pressing process to be made. This improved model was already in general use when Pompeii sank beneath the ashes of Vesuvius. A wall painting in the house of the Vettii demonstrates its operation. The works of Cato and Pliny also provide us with numerous relevant details about it. But we do not need to rely exclusively on ancient written or pictorial evidence. Even today this type of press is still used by a few vignerons in various French wine-growing districts, including the area around Limoux in Departement Aude and in the Touraine. It is also known in the Aurès hills of Algeria.

Admittedly the device had its weak points. If the cable of the windlass broke, something which must have happened not infrequently with increasing loading, no-one standing nearby had even a chance to jumb clear. *Pressoir casse-cou*, "break-neck press", was the name it bore in the Touraine on the strength of such experiences.

Such deadly aspects caused men to start thinking of remedies even in Antiquity. An extremely successful solution was the Greek screw press, described by Pliny and Vitruvius, which apparently came into service shortly before the birth of Christ. In place of the windlass there appeared a huge screw weighted with a stone and passing through the free end of the lever (Ill. 135, 147–149). Turning the screw raised or lowered the weight, thus altering the pressure on the beam. Its operation was safe, quicker and more accurate than with the windlass press. These advantages have given it a long life and wide popularity. The Lotharingian press in the court of the Museum of Viticulture at Speyer demonstrates the size it could reach, as well as its intelligently thought-out construction. Similar examples can still be found in Morocco, Egypt, the Aegean and Italy. A variation of this type was used in

Hungary, as well as on the north shore of Lake Constance, on the Rhine and perhaps also on the Mosel. This variant had a stable wooden holder at the lower end of the screw, which could be loaded with a greater or lesser number of stone weights according to need.

In principle the pressure achieved by the Greek press was determined by the weight lifted by the screw. This limitation too was overcome by the ingenuity of the carpenters concerned with press building. They did it by passing the lower end of the screw through a large nut which was attached rigidly to the ground (Ill. 135, 150). Now the pressure attainable depended solely on the strength of the component pieces. The oldest evidence of this perfected form of beam press – by the wine-growers of Burgundy who called it *pressoir à grand point* – is an illumination from the *Hortus Deliciarum* of the Alsatian prioress Herrad von Landsperg, painted in about 1170. Presses of this type were until a few decades ago highly prized for their working capacity in such places as southern Moravia, around Burgenland in Austria, in certain parts of Hungary, and also on the Côte d'Or.

But in terms of mere numbers in more recent history they have fallen far behind another form of press, which from the end of the Middle Ages was conquering more and more territory in many wine-growing countries, though it was known already in Ancient Rome. Pliny, after his description of the Greek press, relates the exact circumstances of its invention. "It is twenty-two years," he reports, "since men thought of applying the whole pressure from above downwards onto the planks covering the grapes, by arranging the screw in the middle of the press and charging the planks with heavy weights. In this way much shorter planks can be used, and the press may be less cumbersome and of less comprehensive construction." Such advantages gradually gave the various models of the screw press – as it was known – a numerical advantage over the various versions of the lever press. A double screw press, described by Heron of Alexandria in his textbook of mechanics, appears to have come into early use alongside the simple apparatus described by Pliny (Ill. 137, 138).

But its progress may have been less than smooth, for its operation demanded special skill.

*132 Mashing the grapes in front of a screw press. From: Petrus de Crescentiis,* Opus ruralium commodorum libri XII, *Speyer 1493.*

133 *Processing grapes in California towards the end of the 19th century. The co-existence of two processes can be seen clearly: on the left pressing with a high-pressure screw press, and on the right treading in troughs of joined planks, standing on large vertical casks. The heavy jobs (carrying the grapes, treading) are being done by Asians.*

If the two screws were not turned absolutely evenly, the press ran crooked and the juice pressed out of the one side ran into the other, less heavily loaded part of the mash. For this reason it was "indeed much praised, but not much built," as Friedrich von Bassermann-Jordan, an outstanding connoisseur of the subject, has ironically observed. Attempts to increase the number of screws further, were correspondingly even less successful. A five-screw press put into operation in 1775 on the Hoflössnitz estate of the Electors of Saxony can be considered more

as a curiosity. It performed its duties only briefly, and more or less unsatisfactorily.

But the technical principle realized in the screw press has shown itself highly practical. In the nineteenth century it became the pattern for the first industrially-produced models. One can still come across examples of these high-pressure and low-pressure presses in many wine-growing districts today.

In Biblical parables the pressing process became one of the most evocative of symbolic images. The God of the Old Testament, terrible in his rage, crushes the people like grapes. "Why," asks the prophet Isaiah, "is thy apparel red, and thy garments like his that treads in the wine press?" Then Jehovah glories in his deed: "I trod them in my anger and trampled them in my wrath; their lifeblood is sprinkled upon my garments, and I have stained all my raiment." And the Apocalypse threatens the "great wine-press of the wrath of God", which at the end of time will be "trodden outside the city".

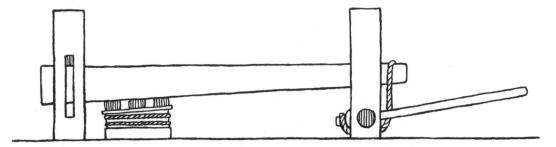

*134 Windlass press. After:* History of Technology, *Vol. II, Oxford* [4]*1967.*

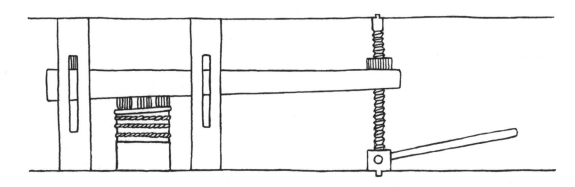

*135 Pressoir à grand point. After:* History of Technology, *Vol. II, Oxford* [4]*1967.*

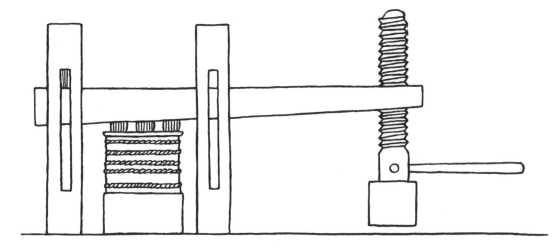

*136 Greek press. After:* History of Technology, *Vol. II, Oxford* [4]*1967.*

The violent imagery of this vision was to fascinate the church fathers, and later mystical thinkers too. The focus of their thought was the redeeming mission of Christ. "He was first pressed, as a grape," wrote St. Augustine. And to St. Bernard of Clairvaux, the most celebrated abbot of the Cistercian Order, itself famous in vine culture, the "rose-coloured blood" of the grapes became in a mystic revelation the blood of Christ.

From such and more ancient beliefs a new motif found its way into sacral art from the twelfth century onwards, in which were linked features of the Old Testament wine-treader with details of the passion of Christ. Standing on the vintage, he himself becomes a grape beneath the beam press of the cross (Ill. 26). His blood flows into the Communion cup. The powerful effect of these representations has at times set them almost equal in importance beside the image of the Crucifixion. In Catholic wine-growing areas they still claim special veneration. After a good harvest grapes are often laid before these pictures.

## 🍇 The Must is Weighed

For by then the wine-grower's uncertainty over the future value of the year's vintage has been essentially resolved. The juice itself flowing from the press, from now until the first fermentation known as must, gives him an indication as to how the wine has repaid the efforts of a year's work. A simple instrument helps him in making this assessment. With it – strangely enough – he weighs the must.

The physical principle lying at the heart of this testing process is simple enough. It is based on the fact that the liquid inside the grapes contains sugar, which during fermentation will turn into alcohol. Sugar is, as we know, heavier than water. Thus as the sugar-content of the must rises, its specific gravity rises too. The realization of this can be glimpsed already between the lines of ancient wine-making literature. The Ancients, however, were unable to find a useful application of it. In the eighteenth century various attempts were made to track down these relationships. In England a saccharometer was in use prior to 1800. The German engineer Ferdinand Öchsle perfected an instrument about 150 years ago.

He must have been a remarkable man. His talents were twofold. A consuming interest in mechanics, linked with a love of music, led him to build the first harmonium in Germany, and its hand-held equivalent, the mouth organ. As a trained goldsmith he had a mechanical workshop set up in Pforzheim. There he invented a method for producing red glass, and the "wheel of life", a forerunner of moving-picture machines. He even tried his hand at distilling spirits. But wine-growers are particularly grateful to him for his invention of the must scale. When immersed in the fluid it shows the number of grams by which a litre of it is heavier than a litre of water. In his honour the degrees in which the instrument is calibrated were named *Öchslegrade*. 80° Öchsle tells the grower that his must has a specific gravity of 1.080. As 5° Öchsle corresponds to one per cent sugar, and 10° Öchsle to one per cent of alcohol, this gravity indicates that the future wine will contain all of 16 per cent sugar or 8 per cent alcohol. In our latitudes that would be considered a good vintage, although more southern zones would not be satisfied. They expect higher values.

## 🍇 Harvest Home

The hope that everything brought to ripeness by work, sun and rain, soil and fertilizer, will now mature in the cellar, and the pleasant anticipation of Winter respite, join together in the celebrations that bring the vintage to a close.

In these celebrations traditional local customs have not infrequently been mixed up with elements dragged in from outside: with courtly refinements or scholarly pottering. Characteristic of this is the appearance of Bacchus in the wine-growing regions of the North and East. In the absence of a direct link with ancient traditions wine-growing people there could not possibly know of him themselves. Nevertheless he appears in every parade – chubby, crowned in vines and inebriated, absolutely in the manner of baroque representations. For doubtless that was how he came to be known to country folk. The particular way they made this ac-

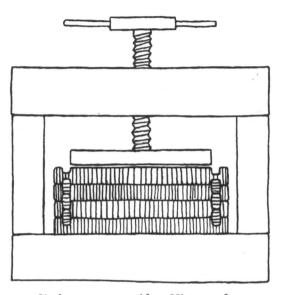

*137 Single screw press. After:* History of Technology, *Vol. II, Oxford* ⁴1967.

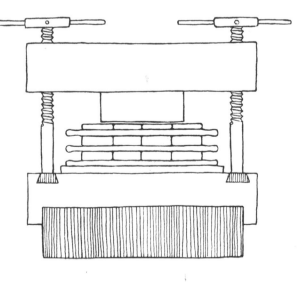

*138 Double screw press. After:* History of Technology, *Vol. II, Oxford* ⁴1967.

quaintance will have probably been through playing the part of extras in intoxicated harvest revels on the lord's estate.

The wine-growers' celebration of 1811 in the Commune of Vevey on the north-east shore of Lake Geneva offered just such a comic mixture of the most heterogenous elements. Its ceremonial procession was made up of a wealth of allegorical figures and mythological scenes, covering every theme from Antiquity to the present, and occasionally producing flashes of unconscious comedy. At the head of the procession came the spiritual and temporal authorities. Behind them followed four fauns with the altar of Bacchus. Then came the high priestess of the heathen deity, followed by Bacchantae dressed in the manner of Antiquity, with ivy wreaths in their hair and tambourines in their hands. They accompanied the young Dionysus, a ten-year-old blond lad. He was carried by four Moors on a barrel, and held in his hands cup and thyrsus wand. Behind him galloped fauns, then came a silen riding on a donkey, followed by satyrs and small boys carrying, besides the attributes of Bacchus, the picture of St. Urban. In colourful sequence now came a jumble of ancient and modern, heathen and Christian: Vulcan with his servants, Joshua and Caleb with the grape, Noah with his wife in wine-growers' garb, shepherds and shepherdesses with lambs, a plough drawn by oxen, the goddess Ceres with altar and entourage, harvesters of both sexes, and finally a lieutenant holding a pitchfork. One of the flags carried had the picture of Ceres, with Bacchus seated on a barrel, under the motto *ora et labora*. At particular places around the town the procession halted and sacrificial ceremonies were conducted before the altars of ancient gods, while hymns of praise got up for the celebrations were sung. Our doubtless highly erudite reporter, describing the procession in a wine almanac, concludes from "the extraordinary similarity of this feast to the Bacchanalia of the Greeks and Romans" that it must be of a "very great age. ... Due to the great attachment of this people to this feast it seems to have been preserved even after the advent of the Christian religion, with the mere addition of St. Urban to the retinue of the heathen god." It is amusing to see the ridiculous contortions that dry book-learning got itself into at the sight of this motley cavalcade. Yet at the same time we forget too readily that even today such apparently "ancient" traditions still come in for miraculous resurrection in such ceremonies.

Wine-growers themselves have celebrated the day since early times without great excursions into Antiquity. Echoes of bacchanalian creatures might possibly have been preserved in the figures of the vineyard-goat and grape-nanny which in Lower Austria were brought along at the close of the vintage. Whether they are really, as an ethnographic compendium of the twenties suggested, "originally related to the goat-like escorts of Bacchus and Dionysus," may remain undecided. Possibly here too some scholarly meddling or aristocratic dilletantism grafted on this later, fantastic chain of reference to Antiquity.

Sebastian Franck in his *Weltbuch* of 1534 recounts a custom then common on the Main. "At the end of the vintage the boys all gather in a field together and from the straw brought there make good hand torches, two apiece. Then at night they go, singing in order, into the town, and thus light the harvest out."

A custom which has grown up in more recent times is the harvest-time choosing of the wine queen, in whose person the charms of a true wine-grower maid should be united with solid knowledge of her subject. This custom has its model in Transcaucasia, where it is said to have a long tradition. When the Georgian farmers have brought in their grapes from the hills and fields they gather for a ceremonial procession led by a wagon on which stands the most beautiful girl of the village, decorated as queen of the harvest.

The fate in store for the young wine is indicated by the famous barrel-hoop dance, which has survived to the present day at certain places in the wine region of Tokay. It is performed exclusively by men, probably in the first place by coopers. An eye-witness who observed the dance at the beginning of the nineteenth century in the inn at Mád, set down on paper a very vivid description: "Tradesmen's apprentices brought into the middle of the room a barrel hoop decorated with the Hungarian national colours, and while performing all manner of feats with it, to the strains of a quite distinctive melody, danced around in a circle. Then they formed a ring and held the barrel hoop high in the air. The best dancer then took up position inside the ring with a smaller hoop. Within the hoop a wooden disc was fastened on which were balanced one or two full wine glasses. Nothing was allowed to be spilled from them as the dancer turned the hoop most rapidly on the index and middle fingers of his right hand, while at the same time he performed involved dance figures and came to sit, and even lie, on the floor."

Such agility speaks for skill in their profession as well. The barrels turned out by these young lads will not have been any worse than their dancing abilities. It is worth seeing these skilful creations in the cellar. Such a visit is most stimulating when the must inside them is bubbling.

*139 Amoretti harvesting and treading grapes. Detail of the "Blue Vase", 1st century, which was found in the Via dei Sepolcri at Pompeii. Museo Archeologico Nazionale, Naples.*

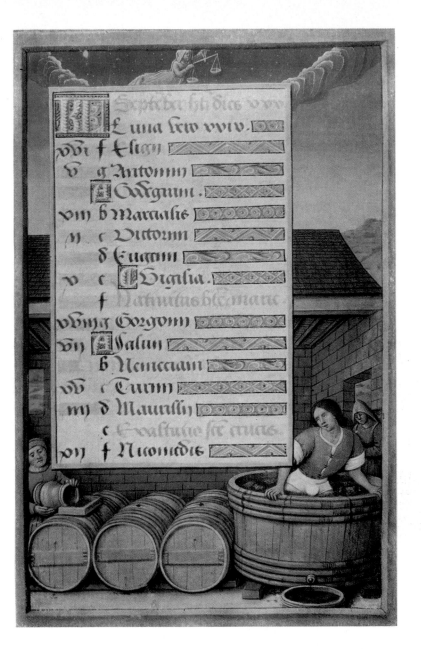

141 *Carrying the grapes in a woven basket, mashing the vintage. In the background left, a screw press. Picture for the month of September from the* Dresdner Gebetbuch, *made in c. 1500, probably in Bruges (artist unknown). Sächsische Landesbibliothek, Dresden.*

140 *Treading the grapes, decanting must into fermentation vats. Picture for the month of September from the* Great Book of Hours of Anna of Bretagne, *by Jean Bourdichon, made between 1500 and 1507. Bibliothèque Nationale, Paris.*

142 *The grapes are carried in hods to the treading vat and there trampled by foot. Picture for the month of September from Queen Mary's Psalter, 14th century. British Museum, London.*

143 *During excavations on an estate at Vathy-petron, Crete, the remains were found of an installation for treading grapes. It is about 3,500 years old and shows already one of the typical forms of the ancient* calcatorium.

144 Traditional wine storage in the Soviet Republic of Georgia, Kolkhoz "Lenin" in Rayon Makharadze. The large pottery vessels are buried up to the rim in the ground, the surface of which is lined with a kind of cement flooring. Jugs fastened to long sticks allow the wine to be drawn out of the storage vessels. The method is similar to the one we know from ancient sculpture and from excavations.

145 Soon these man-high pots will be hardly visible above ground, and will have maturing wine in them. Wine factory at Napareuli, Georgian Soviet Socialist Republic.

146 *Modern pneumatic press (Wilmes press). In the rotating drum lies a long rubber bag which in operation is blown up and presses the mash on its outer side against the perforated cylinder wall. The juice is expressed without breaking the grape pips.*

147 *Two slaves working the screw of a beam press of the Greek type. Ancient relief tablet. Museo Archeologico, Aquileia.*

148 *Beam press of the Greek type in Burgenland, Austria.*

149 The Torggel of Non-nenhorn, on Lake Constance, built in 1591, is one of the few surviving large beam presses in central Europe. It is a variation of the Greek type: the screw at the nearer end of the lever carries a wooden rack which can be loaded according to need.

150 St.Wenceslas pressing grapes. Fresco, c. 1360, on the staircase leading to the Chapel of the Holy Cross of the great tower of Burg Karlštejn, Czechoslovakia.

151 *Screw press from the 19th century, in the Tihany Museum on Lake Balaton.*

152 *Old screw press in action. La Granja on Mallorca.*

153 *Pressing place at Moláoi, Laconia, Greece. The grapes are being pressed in a low-pressure screw apparatus.*

154 *A group of treaders at the wine fiesta in Jerez de la Frontera. The men wear boots studded with nails between which the pips cling and are not broken.*

155 *In Autumn the pressing place becomes the centre of the wine-growing village: vintage on Samos.*

156 *End of the vintage in Hungary during the 1920's. With all ceremony the finest grapes are carried through the village.*

# In Deepest Cellar

## ♟ The Wine Sings

The image of the spirits which live in wine is already worn quite threadbare in story and verse. It is all too easy to apply it to the drinker, to the stages of his decline from amiable tipsiness to shouting and reeling drunkenness. Whatever else happens, whatever the boozer's nature – it is always these imps who are made responsible for the condition and the consequences. And yet nobody has ever seen one, unless perhaps conjured up by drunkenness.

But whoever gets the opportunity can hear them, in the cellar, when the young must begins to turn into wine. During the early stages, in fact, it is better to leave it well alone, as at first it gives off poisonous vapours too rapidly. They stand like a white mist, breast-high between the casks, dangerous for any unwary trespasser. When the violent fermenting ends and the vapour thins, then we can, with an expert to guide us, risk confidently the descent among the spirits.

Not only the novice finds the impression overwhelming. In high vaulted passages that branch several times stand long rows of barrels. Not the sort of little kegs that we see everywhere disappearing into the cellars of pubs or as the last-but-one resting place of herrings. Our future wine has a bigger house fitting to its dignity from the very beginning. These fermentation vats, each of which holds several hectolitres, are mostly made of oak. On their backs they have strange little pottery hats or glass instruments in which our little spirits can be heard constantly bubbling and murmuring. "The wine sings," as they say in France. The sometimes cheerful, sometimes more sinister noise is caused by a gas escaping in bubbles through the water filling the fermentation

locks – the little clay hats. It owes its fleeting existence to the yeast contained in the pressed grape juice or added to it. This microscopic little fungus gets the energy it needs for life by breaking down the sugar in the must into alcohol and carbon di-oxide. In so doing it creates that poisonous mist which at first barred our entry into the cellar.

This whole conversion process is known as fermentation. The knowledge of it is as old as the knowledge of intoxicating drinks, and yet for thousands of years men entertained the most remarkable ideas as to the forces which set it in operation. Cicero, for example, was firmly convinced that fermentation consisted of a weeding out of inferior substances, i.e. the yeast, from the grape juice. Only then could the must, changing to wine, acquire its intoxicating, elevated quality. The nineteenth century, which inscribed on its banners the scientific investigation of nature, was responsible in this field, too, for the breakthrough which led to understanding. Analysis of the fermentation process is connected with such great names as Justus von Liebig and Louis Pasteur. The final explanation was provided by Eduard von Buchner. The importance and value of his investigations was recognized in 1907 with the award of a Nobel Prize.

When the yeast has done its work the now alcoholic liquid is transferred to storage vessels. Is it already wine or is it still must? Many cellarage experts disagree on the matter. In most instances men have now settled for the term young wine. In Mainfranken, however, men still talk of must until it has completed one year of maturing. This doubtless reflects the experience that the strong, full wines in the cellars between the Hassberge and Aschaffenburg need long keeping in order to acquire their distinctive quality.

But must or wine, in any case, now begins its upbringing, which lies chiefly in the hands of the cellarman. For like any adolescent, our young wine has certain traits and features which do not recommend it. It is also occasionally prone to sickness and so keeps its guardians fully occupied.

## 🍷 *Antique Secrets of the Cellar*

In old times the wine was left to itself. In the same vessel where it fermented it was left to mature until such time as it was called for. It cleared "over the yeast", as the expert says today. This involved a natural process of purification in which the alcohol played an important role. Because these wines were drunk quickly – they seldom survived a year – the weaknesses and afflictions of old age were not a serious problem. This very primitive process was probably used already in Egypt. During the sixth century B.C. its existence in Palestine can be demonstrated. It was probably at that time known extensively over the Near East. Its end product will have found buyers mostly among the less well-off. Rich men could afford more painstakingly processed, and therefore more expensive growths.

The authors of Antiquity give information on the means and methods of their production. Cato, for example, recommended drawing off of the fermented fluid from the yeast thirty days after the vintage and leaving it to clear in the cold of Winter. This advice was probably based on the observation that cooling promoted the maturing of the wine. Undesirable elements like albumen and tartar were also precipitated. To mitigate the hardness and sharpness of bitter brews Cato had a special recipe. Small balls of flour should be soaked in a mixture of wine and boiled must and then added to the maturing wine in storage vessels, which after sixty days should be sealed. The results, according to Cato, would be "mild and sweet, of good colour and fine aroma." Columella, too, improved the wine with boiled must. But this ingredient was first to be enriched with the aroma of plants. Iris and fennel he thought particularly suitable by reason of their pleasant scent. If the must were treated with them, then liquid pitch

and turpentine resin were also added as a stabilizing agent. This mixture was stirred in, with sometimes all manner of other herbs in addition. Columella names in this connection varieties of lavender, Illyrian iris, costmary *(Costus)*, myrrh and sweet grasses. This selection was extended with cinammon, saffron and balsam, worked into thick pitch. The reservations aroused by the last-named mixture seem to have been anticipated by the old Spaniard. "Take care that the scent of the stabilizing material be not felt, for this repels the buyer," he advised his reader.

At all events this account teaches us two things. The first is that spiced wines in the style of our vermouth have a long history. The second is that even during Antiquity men were concerned to vary the flavour of wine by adding different ingredients, as well as to lengthen its life and prevent it turning into vinegar. With trodden musts, naturally poor in preservative substances, the latter must have been particularly necessary.

Pliny knew of another method of stabilizing, used by the inhabitants of the island of Kos, which lies before Halicarnassus in Asia Minor. They "mix it generously with sea water. This process was discovered through the thieving of a slave, who in such manner filled up the cask [which before he had secretly partly emptied]. When it is used with white must, it is called white Chier. With other peoples, when prepared in the same way, it is called marinated. But it is called sea wine when the vessels with the must are submerged into the sea. This causes early maturing." In Pliny's time sea water was also put in the wine which came from Clazomenae, a city on the west coast of Asia Minor famed for its ceramic production. The wines of Lesbos had by their very nature a taste of the sea about them, but possibly even with them nature was given a little help.

This method of making wines keep, fell out of favour even during Antiquity. It must have affected the flavour too seriously. The practice of adding resin on the other hand has survived right up to the present. The main region of these resinated wines is the eastern Mediterranean and a part of the Near East. The additives used are the so-called mastic of the pistachio bush, resinous pine wood or spruce needles. These objects are incidentally suggested by

*157 Racking the young wine. From: Petrus de Crescentiis,* Opus ruralium commodorum libri XII, *Speyer 1493.*

158 *Inspecting for colour and clarity.*
*From: Petrus de Crescentiis*, Opus ruralium
commodorum libri XII, *Speyer 1493.*

the thyrsus wand set with cones of the stone-pine, which Dionysus carried as a kind of royal attribute.

In Antiquity these resin wines were also treated not only with pitch but with plaster. This measure also increased its life span – but unfortunately not that of its consumers. Nowadays such additives are nearly everywhere forbidden, because they initiate the formation of sulphuric acid and potassium sulphate, both of which are harmful to health. But in Antiquity men did not know any other way in which to assure the wine its necessary acid content.

Medieval cellar practice took over many of these prescriptions. Additives used still included plaster, salt and resin. The pitch was provided by burning torches which were thrust into the wine. Genuine improvement of the flavour can only have come from the cloves which were used as an additive in the better types. Honey was used to sweeten the must. Thus recommended Petrus de Crescentiis, at least. Whether in so doing he had grasped the connection between sugar content and the percentage of alcohol is not clear from the evidence of his writings. It appears that the cellarmen of his time and of succeeding generations never really understood this relationship. Otherwise there would not have been so many thin, weak wines, requiring drinking at the latest within a year of the vintage.

This meagre stability was not least the result of the numerous organic and inorganic impurities that cloud young wine. Nowadays they are removed in the process of clearing. This can be by transferring the wine from one vessel to another (racking), by spinning the wine in a centrifuge, or by fining. In the latter process the undesirable particles are precipitated out with the help of protein-rich substances, such as egg white, isinglass, carbon and various salts. Subsequently the wine is filtered and finally stabilized by the addition of minerals, acids and acid esters, as well as by short-term changes of temperature. Such processes have resulted from the discoveries of systematic chemical, physical and biological investigation over the last hundred and fifty years.

The medieval cellarman, on the other hand, had to resort to household products when fining his wine. He got protein-rich materials for clearing cloudy wine not only from the whites of hens' eggs, but also from milk, curds and cheese. Even animal blood found a use there. Whether the addition of river pebbles can be considered as a forerunner of the modern process of silica fining, must remain undecided. The effect of the pine cones and peach stones recommended in old textbooks may have been more to stabilize the wine and improve its flavour, than actually clear it.

In central Europe at this time the beneficial effect of sulphur in making wine was probably already known. For there are indications that in certain places it was the practice to burn sulphur, that material surrounded by such alchemical mystery, in the empty barrels. This impregnated the wood with sulphur dioxide. When the container was filled with must or wine it dissolved and became sulphurous acid: $SO_2 + H_2O = H_2SO_3$. In a reaction with the air left in the barrels this oxidized into sulphuric acid. In consequence of this process the amount of oxygen was reduced. The reaction involved can also be expressed in the formula: $2H_2SO_3 + O_2 = 2H_2SO_4$.

The decrease in oxygen hindered the development and multiplication of countless microorganisms, dangerous enemies of the maturing wine. The cellarman of the sixteenth century did not grasp the inner workings of this process, but he knew that sulphur protected the wine from many diseases. It was the chemists and biologists of our times who first discovered the mechanism behind sulphur. This put the wine-maker in a position to improve the process of maturing wine and remove from it the element of health risk involved.

## All Kinds of Wines in Old and New Times

As a result of the shortcomings of old cellar practice many wines were not only dull and dirty but as a result of these defects, their taste, too, often left much to be desired. An additional problem in the growing regions less favoured by the sun was the lack of sweetness. But because cane sugar imported in limited quantities through the Arabs was far too expensive for use as a sweetener in wine, it was often improved with honey instead. This combination must have given the wine a peculiar character. Many of the qualities prized by connoisseurs today must have been missing from it. On the other hand it was certainly thicker, and even sticky. The Thorner product already celebrated gave proof of that.

Attempts were also made to improve the flavour of the wine by the addition of spices. In this, too, men followed antique tradition. The drink known as *Lautertrank* on account of the process of clearing by additives which was the basis of its manufacture, was enjoyed in countless varieties. Some of these are difficult to credit. While Gregory of Tours in the sixth century was chiefly acquainted with honey and wormwood, St. Hildegard of Bingen, the patroness of all cloister spice and herb gardens, listed a whole range of herbs which were still being

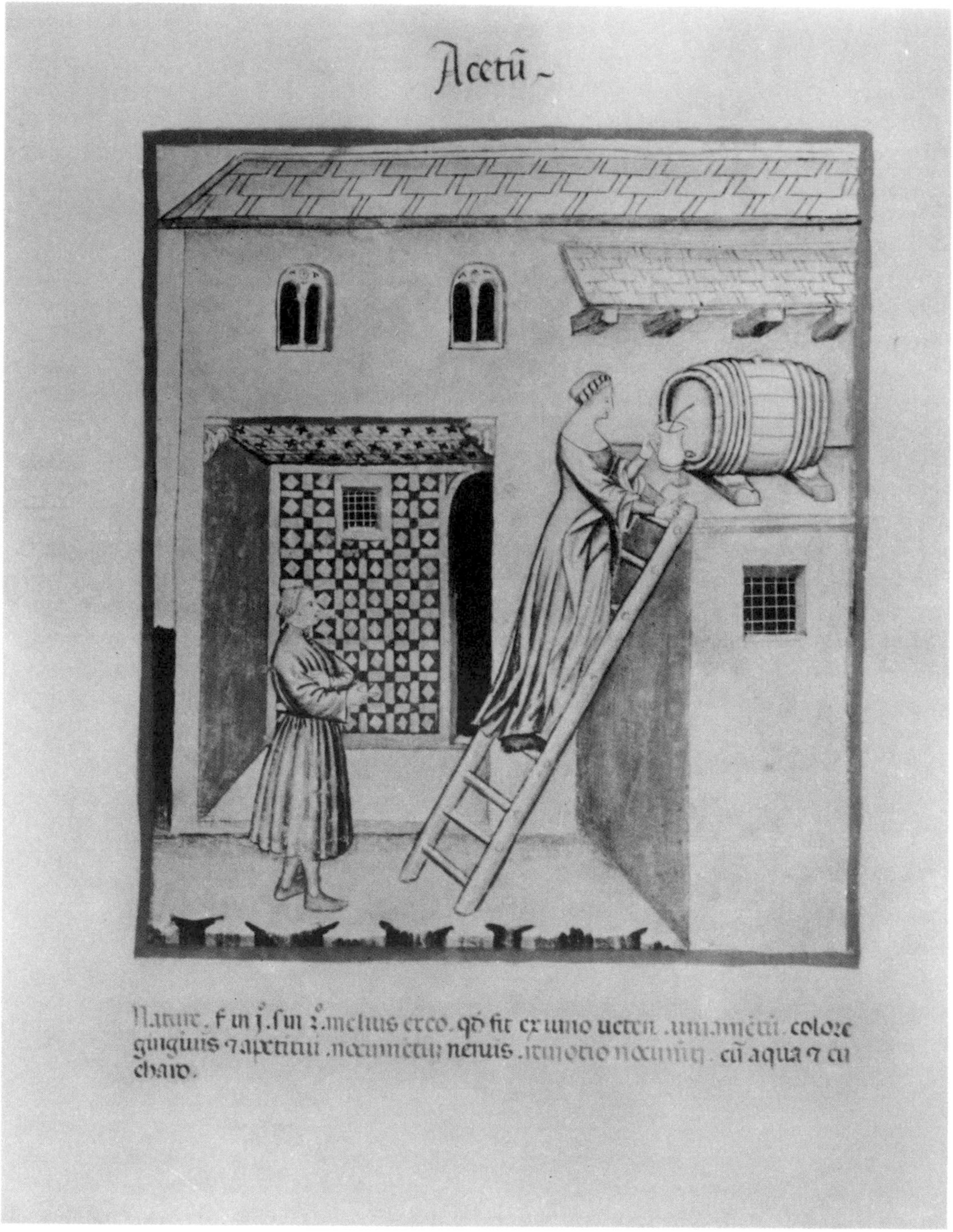


159 *This illustration to the* Theatrum Sanitatis, *a House-Book on medicine from the Orient of the late 14th century, shows the storing of vinegar* (Acetum). *The barrel has been set on a roof, exposed to constant draught, for only the entry of oxygen allows the alcohol to turn into acetic acid. Biblioteca Casanatense, Rome.*

used in wine more than five hundred years later. They included lavender, fennel, sage, ginger, wormwood, lovage, speedwell, and yarrow. Even marjoram, which we now think of, mainly, as a seasoning for sausage and soup, combined its aroma with that of the wine flower. As for the others, hardly anything seems to have been left out. The impression is reinforced when we read from other sources of the same period that gentian, juniper, pennyroyal, peppermint, common mint, spearmint, elder, black elder, rosemary, scabwort, marsh mallow, quince and sloe berries were also prized as additives. The improvement of foreign trade extended the list of possibilities by cinnamon, liquorice and lemons. Pepper was also put in wine, and it was even mixed with crumbs of gingerbread steeped in tropical spices.

Agreste suchus.

*160* Agreste suchus, *a juice from unripe grapes, is being prepared here. It served as a sort of lemonade, but also had medicinal applications. Illustration to the* Theatrum Sanitatis, *Biblioteca Casanatense, Rome.*

The aromatizing was done in one of two ways. Either the additives were boiled in wine and this brew added to the barrels, or they were placed dry into small bags and hung in the full casks.

One of the most celebrated spiced wines of the Middle Ages was the Hippocras. Not only by name was it related to one of the greatest of ancient physicians. It was actually credited with special medicinal powers. Whether these sprang from the additives – cinnamon, ginger, pepper, honey or, more occasionally, sugar – or the alcoholic base, or possibly from a combination of all the ingredients, must be a question for pharmacological investigation. Its descendents live on today in France and in parts of German-speaking Switzerland. Here they understand Hippocras to mean a red wine to which scented herbs have been added.

The situation with medieval claret is rather less clear. It has often been equated with the German *Lautertrank*. Without doubt they were connected by the fact that in their production honey and spices were added. In the course of time, however, claret developed in its own way, more in the direction of the original meaning of its name (Latin *clarus* = clear, light, gleaming). At least some of the wines which in the Middle Ages went by this name or a derivative of it – clairet, clarre, Clarey, Clarry – were characterized primarily by their purity or also their light colour. During the fourteenth and fifteenth centuries the French Chalonnais rosé wine was called "Clairet". Even today this term is applied to the Weissherbst, produced from blue Burgundy and Gamay grapes. It is a pale red wine in the production of which the must is not left to stand on the mash, but in the same manner as with white wines is immediately pressed out.

Every Englishman would protest against such claret. For him the drink of this name is alone and uniquely the deep red wine of Bordeaux. How this came about will never be fully understood. Perhaps many wines from the Gironde in former times had that characteristic rosé tone or that red and white wines were mixed. There are many examples to show that old terms can be very persistent, even when the object they describe changes. Remember the *calcatorium*, the treading trough that later gave its name to all kinds of pressing machines.

Spiced wines have by no means died out. Vermouth, at least as an aperitif, still has a secure future. But other drinks too, nowadays highly popular on tepid evenings or cold nights, cannot totally deny their relation to this or that kind of *Lautertrank* when pressed as to their origins. The genuine *Maibowle* – a kind of claret cup – must contain hand-picked sweet woodruff. It even seems that with the widening variety of ingredients observable today in *cups* the experimentalism of past ages has been surpassed. Everything from pineapple through cucumbers to root vegetables has to venture the leap into the *cup*. A winter hybrid coming from a cross with mulled wine is the so-called firetongs cup. But its effect is not only the result of the red wine in it. For with its burning, melting sugar cap it contains a high percentage of alcohol. It shares this feature with punch, a drink which the British have done much to develop and popularize since the eighteenth century, except that some varieties of this heart-warming drink have renounced wine completely. Schiller, one of the supporters of punch, praised his favourite recipe in a splendid, condensed metaphor:

"Four elements
Inly alloyed
Fashion our being
Model the void.

Press first the lemon's
Succulence tart
Bitter is being's
Innermost heart.

Now with the sugar's
Comforting power
Sweeten the bitter
Soften the sour!

Cover with water's
Bubbling pall
Water embraces
Pacifies all.

Drops of the spirit
Pour in besides
Life to life only
Spirit provides.

*161 Cooper at work. From: Petrus de Crescentiis, Opus ruralium commodorum libri XII, Speyer 1493.*

"Finish it quickly
Before it takes wing
For only when glowing
Refreshes the spring."

This miraculously potent spirit in its various forms will yet engage our attention. But before that we should look at some very particular types and derivatives of wine, whose character is given during the process of fermentation.

Let us recall the observation of Pliny, about how "sea wine" was produced by storing the barrels of must in sea water. The effect thus achieved was roughly similar to the result of a process known today as stopped fermentation. The cellarman of the Middle Ages called such wines "dumb" or "caught".

What happens during such treatment? It would in fact be more to the point to ask what does not happen!

Let us recall that fermentation brings about the conversion of the sugar in grape juice to alcohol. But when alcohol reaches a concentration of 14 per cent by volume it becomes inhibitive to the yeast. It slows down and finally halts its activity and fermentation comes to an end. Any sugar still present remains in the wine and gives it sweetness.

The sugar content of our central European musts is generally not high enough to produce maximum alcohol values, and consequently produces no surplus of sugar. Legislators have therefore permitted the cellarman to make good through various procedures the deficiency in sugar. For his colleagues in Antiquity or the Middle Ages the problem was not so simple. For a long time they had to make do completely without those sweet, white crystals. So some wine producers in Antiquity solved the problem by the trick with the barrels in the sea. At a certain depth a constant low temperature was reached which hindered the activity of the yeast so thoroughly that fermentation practically ceased. In this way the wine retained much of its sweetness. Its alcohol content, on the other hand, was not up to much.

This braking effect was used later too, achieved both by similar and by different means. Men did not shrink from such practices positively dangerous to health as the addition of excessive amounts of sulphur. It is not to be wondered

at that such processes were occasionally banned – but generally only to be gone about another way. For with its sweetness rose the wine's saleability to the public. That is still true today as it was two thousand years ago, even if many an enthusiast of the noble drink would not find it to his liking.

Even so, he may occasionally enjoy a wine from Madeira or from Samos. In doing so he, albeit unknowingly, lends his approval to those indirect descendents of the dumb wines. For these strong drinks are treated before or during fermentation with spirits of wine or possibly with strongly spirited must, thus inhibiting the activity of the yeast. Port also belongs to this family of stopped wines.

To accelerate the development of those flavours which normally develop only with the process of ageing, Madeira is kept in *estufas do sol*, heatable halls with glass roofs. The temperature of these "greenhouses" remains between 40° and 60° centigrade. Even so the wine takes at least two years to mature. Good varieties take still longer. They can contain up to 22 per cent alcohol.

Samos, popular as a ladies' drink, is, in the strictest sense, not wine at all. Its production involves taking freshly pressed grape juice, which for each litre must have a sugar content of at least two hundred grams, and stunning it before the onset of fermentation with spirits of wine. The final alcohol concentration of drinks made in this way can reach eighteen per cent.

In contrast to them Malaga and Sherry with maximum alcohol levels of twenty per cent are known as "fortified" wines. The name of Sherry, a favourite of England, first appears there in 1635, although a similar drink had been popular for nearly 100 years. Only since the end of the seventeenth century does it seem to have reached London from southern Spain in any great quantity. Frequently it first took a voyage halfway round the world to India, for the importers on the Thames believed, not completely unjustly, that such a long sea voyage promoted its ageing. This was probably an experience gained from the importing of South African Cape wine.

The processes underlying the manufacture of Sherry, also known as the Solera system, were elaborated in the seventeenth and eighteenth

centuries, in the region of Jerez de la Frontera. One of its features is that the fermenting must is kept above ground level or in half-sunken cellars. This allows the natural warmth of the surroundings to accelerate the process of fermentation and drive up the level of alcohol. When this stage is finished the delicate treatment begins in a room on ground level. The barrels are stacked in layers, often three high, with the youngest wine in the highest layer (Ill. 164). The containers are only about three-quarters full, and because of the presence of air their contents become covered on the surface with a thick layer of yeast. The cellarman is not perturbed, for he knows that it is precisely this that gives the drink its quite characteristic, slightly bitter bouquet which for the connoisseur means genuine Sherry.

But the yeast is not everything. The wine has still to do much travelling. Wine from the upper layer is mixed with that of the middle layer, while this in turn is passed down to the lowest level. This racking must be performed carefully, for woe betide if the crust of yeast should be damaged. That would endanger the quality of the whole barrel. The descent from layer to layer takes time – a genuine Sherry attends the school of the *solera* for from two to five years. The most valuable types may even complete a dozen years before they go on longer journeys. To all of them, the young and the old alike, is added spirits of wine after they leave the lowest layer, to give them that high alcohol content without which Sherry is not Sherry.

A great dessert wine which does without this doctoring is the Tokay Aszú. Its special processing is based on a technique in which the noble-rotted grapes play a key role. Until recent times they were still trodden, so as not to crush the bitter-flavoured pips. Now the preparation of the Aszú "paste" is given over to a pressing machine. According to old practice the cellarman judges the quality of this pulp by taking out a handful and squeezing it together. If it oozes out thick and viscid, without the pips coming out between his fingers, he is satisfied. Now the wine-making can begin.

The pulp is measured out into small tubs holding from twelve to fifteen kilos and put into vats the capacity of which is measured in *gönci* barrels. This relatively small vessel holds between 136 and 140 litres of fluid. To these vats are now added – for each .gönci barrel – two, three, four or even five tubfulls of Aszú. Exceptionally six may be added. Then the vessel is topped up with normally pressed must, and the fermentation can begin.

Its first, violent stage comes to an end within a few days. When it is over the whole contents are stirred up again and carefully pressed. Formerly the practice was to tip the sodden Aszú pulp into sacks and tread it through a second time. Now the must can settle to its slow secondary fermentation in the gönci barrels. It takes its time, partly because of its high sugar content, and also because of the cool of the deep cellars, cut into the rock. Ageing is also a slow process. A rule of thumb says that an Aszú wine should be kept for as many years as it contains barrels of the nobly rotted grapes. And experience has shown that age becomes it quite exquisitely. That, too, puts it among the very greatest wines of the world.

Positively reverential praise used to be lavished on the samples in the "Tokay Museum" of the Warsaw firm of Fukier. A branch of the Fuggers of Augsburg, they had made a business of keeping and selling the noble drink since the sixteenth century. Up to the Second World War their cellars held thousands of bottles of the absolutely greatest vintages, beginning with 328 bottles of Aszú from 1606. Those fortunate enough to take part in such tastings were often without words to describe the miraculous transformations that the centuries had worked upon the bouquet and aroma of the vine. The scent in the tasting glasses sometimes recalled vanilla, while other bottles and vintages were more evocative of cocoa or strawberries. These occasions must have brought together an extraordinarily rapt but also enraptured company of connoisseurs. Let us in good conscience not grudge them this rare pleasure!

This Tokay has a life of its own. Each year in late Spring, when in the Hegyalja the vines blossom, particularly at night, a fine, sweet scent wafts across the hillsides. In every vintage, down to the oldest bottles, a barely visible fermentation recommences. Tiny bubbles rise through the liquid gold, revealing that all the vintages are celebrating a common birthday. The effervescence is subdued, and familiar almost only to the expert. From another product of the grape, however, we all expect a most visible frothing, for it belongs to it – or, if you wish, makes it champagne.

## ♉ Our Debt to Dom Pérignon

The story of the creation of champagne has become famous. It attributes the invention to Dom Pérignon, who in the second half of the seventeenth century was cellarman of the Abbey of Hautevillers, to the South of Rheims. Some would wish to give equal credit to his brother-in-office, Dom Oudart. Without doubt both men contributed to the discovery, the first certainly more than the second. But properly speaking champagne "discovered" itself. For the vines of the Marne had always sparkled if drunk young enough, by the Spring following the vintage. The reason for this was the continuation of their slowly-ebbing secondary fermentation. Nowadays the same effect is achieved by drawing off the young wine from the yeast straight into the bottles. In western Switzerland such a drink is known as star-wine; when poured into a glass there often remains the pointed pattern of a star when the froth dies away. But what was the contribution of Dom Pérignon?

Firstly the fact that as an outstanding expert he was able to mix the wines from various parts of the Champagne to make a blend which competed successfully with the great French growths. With this technique he created the *coupage*, an unalterable prerequisite of all good champagnes. He also managed to transfer the secondary fermentation from the barrel to the bottle, thus creating the basis for effervescence.

He was able to make great use of a small piece of bark from the cork-oak (*Quercus suber L.*). Cut into plugs, it provided a much more airtight seal than all other stoppers then in use. Dom Pérignon probably had the new material from southern France. He introduced it very successfully into the Champagne, and promoted its spread further afield. But with the bottles both he and his successors for many years were less fortunate. They could not withstand

162 *A common sight on many Georgian plantations are these "pipelines", through which the must is pumped for cellar processing at Wine Factory no.1 in Tbilissi.*

163 *After the first violent fermentation the must is drawn off from the barrel and transferred. Coast of the Peloponnese, Greece.*

164 *Barrels stacked in rows in a* Solera *in Jerez, de la Frontera.*

165 *Gothic vaulting indicates the age of this cellar in Cognac, Charente.*

166 Like huge white bells the upper parts of the fermentation tanks rise from the metal floor in the sparkling wine factory at Kishinev, Moldavian Soviet Socialist Republic.

167 A view of the state cellars of Budafok, Budapest, set up along the most modern lines. The wines are stored behind tiled walls in large concrete tanks.

168 Giant tanks of stainless steel are increasingly characteristic of modern wine manufacture. They are used as fermentation vats and for storing. To the right, a grape-picking machine. California.

169 *Satyr with wine skin. Bronze statuette as a well decoration at Pompeii. Museo Archeologico Nazionale, Naples.*

170 *Perhaps the wine in these amphorae came from Gaul or Iberia. It failed to reach its destination in Italy: divers brought the vessels up from a sunken Roman ship. Civico Museo, Albenga.*

171 The wooden well-lining of a Roman citadel near Rheingönheim, Ludwigshafen, first half of the 1st century. In its construction parts of unserviceable old barrels were used, among which Roman coopers' marks can still be made out: one of the old walnut staves carries the stamp of the workshop of COBNERT (US). Weinbaumuseum in the Historisches Museum der Pfalz, Speyer.

172 A servant draws wine from a large voluted crater. Etruscan tomb painting from the Tomba della Caccia e della Pesca, c. 520–500 B.C. Tarquinia.

the increasing pressure of the fermentation. The constant fear of being injured by the explosions must have been less than pleasant for the workers in the champagne cellars. Everyone knows what deadly and dangerous wounds are inflicted by flying glass splinters. Between 25 and 40 per cent of the bottles burst! Improvements in foundry techniques during the last hundred years brought a partial remedy. The control of the sugar content of the wine helped even more and the loss today is half of one per cent.

Champagne has that name chiefly in the land of its birth, which enjoyed a monopoly of production and therefore unchallenged exports until well into the eighteenth century. The secrets of its manufacture came to Germany only after the armies of Napoleon had withdrawn. But it seems that the officers of the Great Army had made the new drink popular in the occupied areas. Champagne factories now began to spread outside France. Sparkler was produced in Germany from 1820. Besides bottle fermentation the tank fermentation process has been developed, whereby the young wines are kept to mature in large stainless steel containers. This is the process adopted in sparkling-wine factories, among which those of the Soviet Union enjoy a particularly high reputation (Ill. 166). In German-speaking regions the product of this cellar treatment is not known as champagne, but *Sekt*. The basic reason for this is not only French anxiety to restrict the older term to their own product alone. So why *Sekt*?

## 🍷 Did Falstaff Drink Sekt?

There is an anecdote which attributes the christening of *Sekt* to the German actor Ludwig Devrient. On a November evening in 1825, it is related, he burst into the Berlin winehouse of Lutter and Wegener, the role of Falstaff still in his head after a performance of Shakespeare's *Henry IV*, and shouted, "Give me a cup of sack, rogue! Is there no virtue extant?" (Shakespeare's translator August Wilhelm Schlegel rendered "sack" by the Germanized coinage *Sekt*). The waiter proceeded to bring him in customary manner his well-loved sparkling wine, never having heard of course of that Spanish wine with the English name which fat

Sir John had in fact ordered. With the course of time the celebrated mistake led to all German sparkling wine being known by the name *Sekt*.

Which may or may not be true. But what sort of wine was the original "good sherris-sack"? In a dispute with Prince John Falstaff seems unable to find words enough to describe its effect:

"It ascends me into the brain; dries me there all the foolish and dull and crudy vapours which environ it; makes it apprehensive, quick, forgetive, full of nimble fiery and delectable shapes; which, deliver'd o'er to the voice, the tongue, which is the birth, becomes excellent wit. The second property of your excellent sherris is, the warming of the blood... If I had a thousand sons, the first human principle I would teach them should be, to forswear thin potations and to addict themselves to sack."

To judge by the old reprobate's panegyric, this sack must have been a truly racy wine. The addition of sherris points to its Spanish origin, or more precisely to Jerez de la Frontera. In this direction points also the explanation which is still most widely accepted today. It sees the English "sack" as a derivative of the Spanish *seco*, or dry. *Vino seco* is a bitter, fully-fermented wine with no remaining surplus of sugar. So far, so good. The problem is that English sacks were by no means all of this kind. The *Philocotonista* of Thomas Heywood, published in 1635, lists under "all kinds of sacks" such types as Malligo, Charnio, Cherry, Canary, Leatica, Frontiniack as well as Petersee-mee (a nice bowdlerization of Pedro-Ximénez, a grape variety from southern Spain). But most of these wines were sweet. This has led William Younger to offer another explanation. He argues that the word could also have as its origin the Spanish *sacar*, meaning to "stretch out, bring out", or in the figurative sense, "to export". Thus in the course of time the *vinos...sacar al mar* mentioned in a Spanish letter of 1491 over the trade of Jerez, would have been altered by the English into a form more accessible to their tongues. But Younger goes on to suggest a second possibility, a derivation from the Spanish *saco*, a bag or sack. This would be in reference to a characteristic method of extracting the must – treading a sack filled with grapes. Perhaps the English term contains echoes of both associations. Falstaff's Sherris-sack would then

*173 Wine-growing woman. Relief carving from the stand of a storage barrel from Gimmeldingen in the Palatinate, c. 1750. Weinbaumuseum in the Historisches Museum der Pfalz, Speyer.*

*174 Cooper. Relief carving from the stand of a storage barrel from Gimmeldingen, c. 1750. Weinbaumuseum in the Historisches Museum der Pfalz, Speyer.*

be identifiable as an imported wine from Jerez, whose grapes were trodden rather than pressed. Schlegel's original translation and Devrient's thirst would thus be responsible for grafting the German *Sekt* onto a very remarkable old distinguished wine family!

## ♟ *Firewater*

Before we return to wine, let us make another small digression upon the grandsons of the grape. They are a stalwart band. During the nine hundred years of their existence they have adopted many new members whose origins lie rather in corn fields, sugar-cane plantations, rice paddies or even in potato fields. More recently too there have appeared among them some genuine homunculi, who have sprung from the chemical retorts of industry.

Indeed the whole tribe from its very beginnings has had an affinity with the alchemist's kitchen, for their birthplace is the distiller's alembic. The first one in which wine was "burned" was probably set up in about 1100 in Salerno. Here, where the handed-down knowledge of Antiquity mixed with Arab-Saracen scholarship, there grew up at about this time the leading medical school of the Middle Ages. The remarkable degree of freedom of thought which they enjoyed for their epoch opened up new possibilities for investigating natural sciences. Certainly not the most momentous result of this progress, but without doubt one of the richest in consequences, was the production of "burning water". This is the literal meaning of the term *aqua ardens* by which the new substance was known to the scientific world. The expectations made of it are conveyed by the name which appeared a little later – *aqua vitae*, or "water of life" – to describe this several-times-distilled, highly-concentrated alcohol. If you questioned the Danes on their tastes, you would find that even today among the hard drinks they prefer one with a very similar title.

The manufacturing secrets of this highly attractive new stuff were not long preserved. Soon it was known to all the alchemists in Italy, and not much later to all the apothecaries. A Spanish physician named Arnaldus de Villanova, doctor to kings and popes, was

the first, towards the end of the thirteenth century, to give precise instructions for the manufacture of liqueurs by distilling herb and spice wines. Apothecaries rapidly adopted highly-concentrated alcohol in their prescriptions, ascribing to its decoctions particular value in times of plague. They would have given those hovering in their death agonies at least a passing feeling of warmth and false security.

Generally speaking the promotion of spirits within medicine was only a side stream in their development. Their main course was fixed by Arnaldus de Villanova, if not earlier. The apothecaries of Italy began with Rosoglio, a liqueur whose flavouring elements were raisins and, strangely enough, the flesh-eating sundew *(Drosera)*. In about 1330 the secret of the new process reached Paris, and from there spread rapidly across the whole of Europe. Gradually the sweetening agents, at first very powerful, were reduced. At the same time liqueur won a powerful competitor in brandy, or "burned wine". In about 1400 ingenious minds finally succeeded in getting strong alcohol from fermented corn. Now the way was opened for its mass production even where wine-growing was almost or totally unknown. Almost every brewery tried its hand at this new line. A wave of hard liquor was unleashed, the effects of which were overwhelming. City policing ordinances and warnings from physicians were equally ineffective in stemming the tide of drinking fever. Where distilling was officially outlawed the number of secret stills merely grew instead. The "Schnaps Devil", as fifteenth-century pamphlets thundered, had taken control. Inferior quality products caused severe damage to health; but even such evil consequences did nothing to confine the general boozing fever. William Hogarth's gruesome pictorial protests attempted to shake people from their alcoholic stupor. But men drank on. Some because they could afford to stumble from one drunken fit to the next; others to find a little oblivion in their misery. Gin dealt them all the coup-de-grace.

The supply was great, and the number of varieties multiplied. In extending the family of liqueurs monasteries too were busily engaged. In their gardens the plants blossomed which gave Chartreuse and Benedictine their aroma. From these beginnings there grew a fantastic

175 *Distillers' garden. From: Brunswick,* Liber
de arte distillandi, *1512.*

wealth of varieties. On the harder side, among
corn-based spirits, the lead was taken by gin,
vodka, whisky – already befuddling the court of
the Scottish kings at the beginning of the sixteenth century, under the name *usquebagh* – and
geneva, which owes its characteristic flavour to
juniper berries in the still. From the fermented
mash of these fruits alone Steinhäger was and
still is distilled. This origin puts it in the group
of products whose most famous representatives
are Kirsch and Slivovitz.

At the head of all distillates, cognac occupies
an unchallenged position. Its distinguishing
quality is the achievement of generations. But
its creation in the first place is really to be explained by economic factors. The region where
the wines are made from which cognac is distilled
was once severely disadvantaged with regard to
other vine growing districts of France. During
the 1630's the wine-growers of the Saintonge
and Angoumis sent a petition to their lords beg-
ging for a reduction of the taxes on their wines.
They pointed out the long distance which their
goods had to travel down the Charente to reach
the trading centres lying on the Atlantic. In
contrast with them the wine-growers of the
Gironde, for example, with their centre at Bordeaux, enjoyed an enormous advantage. Their
transport costs were considerably less.

The petition was in vain. Then, in 1709, a
severe winter led to the freezing of most of the
vines in the Saintonge. But the wine-growers did
not give up. Without official assistance they
brought their plantations back into order and
from then on they concentrated on preserving
their products by distilling them. Thus they
outflanked the competition of the Gironde, and
created for themselves a monopoly of world
renown. The town of Cognac lying on the
Charente gave the product its name. The wines
that go into it are mostly from the grape Enrageat
Blanc. They lend the end-product a particularly
fine aroma. Long experience has proved that the
best brandies come chiefly from small wines.
Big vintages, on the other hand, produce heavy,
over-rich concentrates.

Distillation is conducted in two stages. The
result of the first is the *brouillis*, an extremely
opaque liquid (French *brouiller* = to muddy,
cloud) with an alcohol content of thirty per
cent. A second process gives a clear liquid of

sixty per cent proof, which the distiller poetically calls *le coeur*. This heart, which in a further process is reduced to a wholesome concentration, gains with keeping. Three stars mean that it has matured for one year. Supérieur has spent at least three years, Réserve four and the great Napoléon at least five years in the cellar.

## In Praise of Coopers

Which brings us back to those lofty rooms where we left the young wine in its storage casks. In the meantime it has been gathering character. Large firms nowadays give it the chance to do so in stainless steel or polythene-lined tanks or in huge concrete tanks lined with glass or an inert synthetic material (Ill. 167, 168). A walk through one of these scrupulously clean wine factories gives an impression of the importance modern technology has acquired in the business of the cellarage. One sees few workers there. The most important person is at the control and mixing installations, where filling and blending are supervised.

But by no means all wines mature in this manner. Many old and distinguished cellars still prefer the barrel. Its roughly two-thousand-year-old history doubtless will enjoy a long continuation. To a limited extent the same might be true of its older brothers and one-time competitors, the clay jar and the leather skin. These two types of container have survived sporadically along the coasts of the Mediterranean and in Transcaucasia.

While the forerunners of the Spanish and North African goat-skin wine bag have all mouldered long since, and only a few chance pictures have survived to prove their former use (Ill. 169), the pottery relics of old cellar practice have come down to us in their thousands. The museums around the Mediterranean and the Black Sea possess whole stores of amphorae and jugs. They survived in the graves along the Nile, under the ruins of ancient inns and farmhouses, and also in the hulks of sunken ships (Ill. 170). Only their contents have vanished. Even preserved in mint condition they would seem quite foreign to the connoisseur of our times and not just because of the peculiar methods of their production. The prep-

aration of the containers themselves gave the contents what modern palates would consider an unusual flavour. It involved painting their insides, to seal them as much as possible, with a thin layer of oil or resin. Perhaps the latter process was historically the predecessor of resinated wine. When men noticed that the additive increased the stability of the contents, they started putting it directly into the wine. However this resin was applied, a distinct flavour must have always been imparted to the drink.

With the keeping of wine in barrels the flavour at first must have been no different, for the seams of wooden vessels which had been in use north of the Alps from the end of the Bronze Age, required smearing with a sticky material. As long as pitch was used for this purpose the giving of a particular flavour was hardly to be avoided. The results were similar to the *vinum picatum* of the Allobroges. The evil was only surmounted little by little. The Gauls, apparently, had managed it earlier, for the Romans, who took over the new storage technique from them during the period of the emperors, did not complain of any such shortcomings. It appears that the barrel made at first only hesitant progress in the South. Pliny still seems more or less unacquainted with it, for he remarks in his *Naturalis historia*, not without wonder: "In the Alps men store wine in wooden vessels, surrounding these with hoops, and in the cold moreover use fire to prevent freezing." But earlier than him the geographer Strabon had reported on the new type of vessel in the wine-maker's cellar.

North of the Alps, he relates, men have seen wooden wine barrels bigger than houses. Possibly here he had been taken in by his informants. For the few pieces preserved from Antiquity are considerably smaller. This does not exclude the possibility that such remarkably capacious barrels might have existed. But the probability is that the state of the craft at that time set certain limitations on their size.

Good craftsmanship brought a remedy for this in the Middle Ages. Its masters – the coopers – united skill in woodworking with knowledge of wine-making. They met the demands of cellarage and the wine trade with a range of all shapes and sizes, from playful dwarflike table kegs to huge tuns capable of holding hundreds of thousands of litres. No wonder that they

176 *Offering a toast. From: Petrus de Crescentiis,* Opus ruralium commodorum libri XII, *Speyer, 1493.*

prized their own trade above all others. "I hold my craft for the finest there can be under the sun," says Master Martin the cooper in a tale from the German writer Ernst Theodor Amadeus Hoffmann's *Serapionsbrüder*, haranguing the old Squire Spangenberg.

"Do you think, maybe, that it's enough to drive the hoops down over the staves to make a barrel hold together? Ah, as if it were not a fine and splendid enough thing in itself that our craft calls for knowledge of how to nurture and tend that splendid gift of Heaven, noble wine, so that it may flourish, and fill us with all its strength and sweetness, like a true, glowing spirit of life. But then comes making the barrel itself. Mustn't we first compass and measure everything, if the construction is to work? We must be masters of reckoning and of measurement, for how else can we know the proportions and capacity of the barrel? Ah, Sir, it does my heart good when I bring a nice barrel like that on to the end bench, after the staves are got nice and ready with the pinching ring and the crowbar, and the prentices swing their hammers – clip, clap, clip, clap – down they come on the drivers! Aye, that is music in my ears. There it stands, a well turned-out barrel; and well may I look round me a little proud, when I take the graver to hand and carve my sign, known and esteemed by all fine wine masters, in the bottom of the barrel." After which, as is known, Spangenberg's son Konrad could do nothing else but study coopering in Martin's workshop, incognito, and finally, after a number of trials and tribulations, win the heart and hand of the master's daughter.

The stout craftsman's song of praise calls for completion. For he forgot one thing which nowadays particularly impresses us in the art of the old coopers. The ends of their barrels are often real works of folk carving art. But this ornamentation came into fashion after the times which E. T. A. Hoffmann had in mind. Early examples come from the seventeenth century. They carry the coat of arms of the proprietor (Ill. 180), or frequently pictures of the wine Saints. The eighteenth and nineteenth centuries went beyond these thematic boundaries. The cooper and wine-grower now make themselves heard, and even occasionally put themselves into the picture. The revelling boozer also be-comes the target of some good-natured satire (Ill. 183). One carver sets in the mouth of the lord of all grapes an imaginary appeal to a parsimonious old woman, which shows the abomination in which wine-growers held all those who stinted in their drinking:

"I, Bacchus, tell thee, worthy friend
Be with good wine no miser
Drink oftener, though with modesty
And prove yourself the wiser
Than this old pinching, scrimping dame
Full of remorse we find her
The devil carries her to Hell
Her wine stays all behind her."

Below is depicted the boozing god, pointing a moralizing finger at the gruesome wheelbarrow ride into the jaws of everlasting damnation (Ill. 181).

An interesting document of its times is a Palatinate barrel top which unites in its design left-bank Rhine civic pride with democratic consciousness (Ill. 182). That much is indicated by the crowning emblem – the scales of Justice under the Jacobin cap – and the dating in the text above it: "In the tenth year of the Republic we hoped for a good wine ..." The wish was fulfilled, we read in the remainder of the text. The vintage of 1802 was "small, but strong". It probably survived longer than the First French Republic, of which the Palatinate was then a part. It died on May 18, 1804, when Napoleon had himself declared hereditary emperor.

## Barrels as Big as Houses

Two often-quoted episodes from the Great German Peasant War give us our earliest glimpse of some very remarkable achievements of the cooper's art. In 1525 insurgents stormed the Kestenburg, a property of the Prince Bishop of Speyer (in 1832 under the name of Hambacher Castle it was again the scene of bourgeois revolutionary activities). In the kitchens and cellars they helped themselves liberally to everything which they had been forced to surrender in tithes to their spiritual lord. On this occasion a giant tun, built in about 1500 and holding a good hundred thousand litres of wine, was drunk dry. At the same time a similar fate met the only slightly smaller tun at the Abbey Eberbach in the Rheingau, again at the hands of revolutionaries. Reading such reports one must bear in mind the large numbers of the peasant armies. Not far from Kestenburg near Saverne, Duke Anton of Lotharingia on May 16 and 17, 1525, had his mercenaries slaughter those Alsatian insurgents who had surrendered to him. Eighteen thousand peasants, according to the horrifying account, were killed in the two days. The throng which settled its account with the Bishop of Speyer – albeit in a much more humane way – will not have been much smaller. Thus the amount of wine drunk by each person in the cellars of the Kestenburg, will not have been as much as first expected.

But why did provincial princes promote the building of such prodigious casks? The answer is given in part by the above account. The containers were designed specifically for holding the tithe wine of these great landlords' peasant underlings. The wine subsequently found its way into the cellars and kitchens of the staff in their service. They received it, along with other foodstuffs, as payment in kind. It was also drawn by officers, sub-officers and the rank and file of standing armies as part of their provisions. Finally it was given as an honorarium to those who had performed special services for the landlord.

Most of these huge barrels have not survived. In later years, following the abolition of feudal dues, they suffered from a lack of anything to put in them. Without special preservation methods they were then almost impossible to save. Many had already been laid in ruins by acts of war. With some exceptions, there remain now only the pictures of these richly-decorated masterpieces of coopering. The tuns of Heidelberg were a particular attraction but only the third and last can still be visited. Skilled coopers built this veritable "house of wine" in 1750. With its approximate capacity of 230,000 litres it outstrips both its forerunners quite considerably for size. Old Strabon would have liked it, as he would

also the tun which August the Strong in the 1720's had assembled in his mountain fortress of Königstein. With its capacity of 254,000 litres it was the biggest of which a German provincial prince could ever boast. Like its two older brothers which during the seventeenth century stored wine on the same spot, it rotted and collapsed. An idea of its dimensions is provided by a contemporary print (Ill. 177). Particular sensation seems to have been aroused by the dance floor which balanced upon the back of the prodigious tub.

## ♟ The Cellar and Its Law

Such dinosaurs required cellars to match. They were enormous vaults. Beside them the dimensions of the normal wine cellars of the time seem modest indeed although they held much, much more, for they countered height with length. Men worked at them over hundreds of years, driving new tunnels and galleries.

"The whole town is so tunnelled and mined
Cellars so wide and deep you find
Quite filled up with the cool wine
Could not be cooler, or more fine,"

reports Wolfgang Schmeltzl in 1548 in his tribute to Vienna. We can be sure that the same was true of many other places both large and small, whose citizens lived from wine-growing and the wine trade.

The peasant, on the other hand, had his own type. In older times he rarely kept his wines in the house. They lay in cellars near the vineyards or at the edge of the village. In places where the power of the mechanical press was applied, the cellars are often linked with the press house. This arrangement can be seen in Austria, parts of Czechoslovakia (Moravia, Slovakia), Hungary and Rumania. Here, too, the simple pit cellar is also very common, dug out of the clay, sunk into limestone or lava, and occasionally decorated with naive reliefs. Wherever they appear they are a sign that at this place grapes were formerly pressed only by treading. Another very widespread and certainly very old method of storing is the above-ground stacking of barrels. We observed it in the soleras of Jerez de la Frontera and it can still be seen in southern Europe, in the eastern Mediterranean and in Transcaucasia (Ill. 186). Generally the method is connected with a fermentation procedure not unlike the Spanish one in certain respects.

Finally, the inheritance of Antiquity has been preserved in two places in Europe separated from each other by thousands of kilometres. One of these regions has already attracted our attention, Georgia, where even today much wine is matured and kept in large containers sunk up to their mouths into the floor (Ill. 144, 145). Similar treatment is given in its youth to Montilla, an excellent Spanish wine which grows on the naked limestone hills south of Córdoba. The solera method is used, as with Sherry, to bring it to a high level of perfection. Before it is stacked, however, it must spend a certain time in *tinajas* – earthenware vessels that are taller than a man. In shape they are very similar to ancient storage vessels.

Excavations in the Near East and Greece have shown that by Roman times cellarage of wine already looked back on long traditions and experience. Clay tablets found in Lagash, 4,500 years old, describe the storage place of wine as a kind of basement under houses. And in the depths of the royal castle at Nimrud, the metropolis of Assyria in the ninth century B.C., was a fully-equipped cellar with four rows of large terracotta vessels. Cuneiform documents show that their alcoholic contents were expressly reserved for wetting the throats of the king's Kassite male voice choir. We all know how much such choral societies can get through!

One of the castle lords of Mycenae had made similar provision for himself, his men and his guests. In a subterranean room, fourteen metres long, stood three rows of handsome crocks, one along the wall and two across the centre. Excavated potsherds allow us to suppose the existence of a further row against the other long wall. The total capacity of this store is calculated by archeologists at about six thousand litres. Fourteen times more than this could have been kept in the cellar of a villa built in the first century, excavated near ancient Stabiae at the foot of Vesuvius. When the Romans went in for something they did it properly and well – above all because of the solid profit it brought in.

But to come back to the present. First of all, a word to people visiting cellars. Here in these vaults special rules apply. No smoking: tobacco smoke will upset both the wine and the cellarman. It will be badly received if souvenir hunters try to remove from the wall a part of its coating of black mould; as "cellar cloth" it helps to regulate the humidity of the air. And finally let nobody knock on the barrels. Certain "cellar laws" prescribed a sound thrashing for such reprehensible curiosity. The wine must not be disturbed. Look at it another way: imagine allowing oneself an experimental tap at one's purse, and having regrettably to discover that it is empty. So what business of the visitor's is it how many of the barrels are full!

However reticent the owner may be in these matters, when it comes to presenting his product he will spare neither time nor trouble. No one who really wishes to get to know the gift of Dionysus, should miss such a tasting in the cellar. Nowhere is wine so natural as when drunk straight from the barrel. In no other circumstances does it reveal so intensively all its qualities of colour, bouquet and taste. And how talkative the wine-maker now becomes! One feels he has turned into a poet, listening to the inexhaustible wealth of adjectives that pour from him as he expounds the qualities of his charges. One is pleasant, firm and vigorous, the next is polite, fruity and glowing, another is full-bodied and fiery, and, to end with, a bouquet-rich, mature and elegant growth to crown the tasting session. One weighs up the wine and the word for a long time, half baffled by such cellar lyricism. One thinks with a trace of envy of those two excellent masters of wine-tasting which Sancho Panza, himself respected as a stout drinker in La Mancha, could boast among his forebears. Their greatest feat was of a quite remarkable nature:

"They were both given to taste from one barrel of wine, and begged for their opinion as to the condition, nature, quality or deficiency of the wine. The one tried it with the tip of his tongue, the other did no more than sniff it. The first said that the wine tasted of iron, and the second, that it tasted more of cordovan leather. The proprietor said that the barrel was clean, and that the wine had received no addition, from which it could have acquired the taste of iron or leather. Unimpressed by this the two excellent wine tasters held to their opinion. With the passage of time the wine was all sold, and when the barrel was cleaned there was found a small key inside, hanging from a thong of cordovan leather."

This story has gone the round of many countries, changing narrator and characters. Neither has the disputed object in the dregs of the barrel always remained the same. But the descendants of these outstanding "wine biters" – as their fraternity is known in Austria – are still among us. At tastings one can entrust oneself with pleasure to their expert guidance.

## ☗ Woe to the Adulterator

We should not expect them to be able to tell us anything about the flavour of those vintages over which Sancho Panza's ancestors disputed. We were puzzled enough as to the sensations which the varied bouquet of fifteenth-century spiced wines would have produced on tongue and palate. But as to the properties of some other varieties we have no information whatsoever. Nobody now can tell us the details that distinguished "heunischer" wine (being of low quality with a high water content and hard husks) from Frankish. All we can glean from old reports is that in German-speaking territories the second was set far above the first, and consequently brought higher prices. Reaction was thus correspondingly severe when a cellarman, wine merchant or innkeeper dared to mix the two varieties together and sell them as "Frankish". And yet such tricks were not unusual.

A *Lexicon of Deceits* from the eighteenth century describes further practices of this nature, which may have injured many a drinker in his wallet, if not his stomach. Its author must have studied the adulterators closely. They deceive their customers, he writes, by bulking out the wine with water or good growths with bad ones; by falsifying its taste and colour with additions of sulphur; by using unslaked lime for the same purpose; by putting inferior musts into barrels containing yeasts from high-quality Spanish, Italian, Hungarian or Rhenish growths,

*178 Must barrel* (Mostlotte) *from Landau in the Palatinate, made in the mid-19th century. On the screw above the tap sits a cooper, apparently finding the new vintage quite to his liking. Weinbaumuseum in the Historisches Museum der Pfalz, Speyer.*

179 Cooper with a half-finished Bota (contents 516 litres) of American oak. Jerez de la Frontera.

180 Barrel top from 1661 with the names of the owning couple. Weinbaumuseum in the Historisches Museum der Pfalz, Speyer.

181 Drinker goes to damnation. Carved barrel top, c. 1800. Weinbaumuseum in the Historisches Museum der Pfalz, Speyer.

182 A document from revolutionary times: a barrel top dated in the tenth year of the First French Republic, of which the Palatinate was then a part. Weinbaumuseum in the Historisches Museum der Pfalz, Speyer.

183 Three very jolly boozers in a wine-house, on a carved barrel top from 1830. Weinbaumuseum in the Historisches Museum der Pfalz, Speyer.

184 *Storage barrels in the State Wine Cellars at Eger, Hungary. In these underground vaults, in places over a kilometre long, lie huge tuns. Some of them hold about 17,000 litres.*

Willkommen herein hier ist ... sein,
Wo man die Zung thut la...en.
Hier gibt es Wein der schme...ket fein,
Allein hüt dich vor Schaden.
Bachus der wacht, gibt fleisig acht,
Wie man sich hier anstellet,
Klopfst du an's Fass, und er hört das,
Sein Urtheil er gleich fället.
Der Küferknecht, das Küfe recht,
Schon längst hat ausstudirt,
Das wird Er dir gleich geben hier,
Wie m Vorwitz es gebührt.

188 *Wine cellar door with Gothic wrought-iron fittings. Schwäbisch-Hall.*

187 *A Palatinate cellar law from the second half of the 18th century. Weinbaumuseum in the Historisches Museum der Pfalz, Speyer. The warning reads as follows:*
*"Welcome inside, t'is good to bide*
*Here where the tongue doth lead thee*
*Here there is wine which tasteth fine*
*Only of mischief heed thee.*
*Bacchus on guard keeps vigil hard*
*How thee thyself do carry*
*Knock you on't vat and he hears that*
*His judgement will not tarry.*
*The cellar wight hath cellar right*
*A long time known and learned*
*And on the spot will give thee what*
*Thy meddling hath earned."*

186 *Many of the wines grown in the state farms of Georgia mature above ground, in large halls.*

189 Good Burgundy is tasted from a silver tastevin. Here the tasting is taking place on the spot where it grows: near Beaune, in Burgundy.

190 Burgundian tastevins. Wine collection Rauner, Radebeul near Dresden.

191 Cellar tasting, from the barrel. Châteauneuf du Pape, Côte d'Or.

192 *Tasting in the beautifully furnished testing rooms of the firm "Moldavino", Moldavian Soviet Socialist Republic.*

193 *Wooden, richly carved wine bottle from the Moldavian Soviet Socialist Republic.*

194 *He swears his wine is the best that grew around Tbilissi this year.*

195 *Amoretti as wine-merchants. Mural in the house of the Vettii, Pompeii.*

196 *Wine-merchants tasting on the quayside (probably at Dordrecht, Holland). Painting by Jan van Goyen, first half of the 16th century. Musée de Picardie, Amiens.*

197 In the larger medieval communities there were special warehouses for the wines kept by the council and the merchants. Thanks to the efforts of conservationists some of these buildings have survived to the present, as, for example, this fine timbered house at Henkersteg in Nuremberg, built in the mid-15th century. Since 1528 it served as a wine warehouse.

198 Cargo boat with wine in front of the Pescheria on the Canale Grande in Venice.

199 *This straw-work wreath set with brush, hung outside an inn in Lower Austria, indicates that here they sell* Heuriger: *that is, wine which is still in the first year of its maturing. After the next vintage it will become the Verdige (last year's), and from the third year it will be the Alte (the old one). Weinbaumuseum, Krems.*

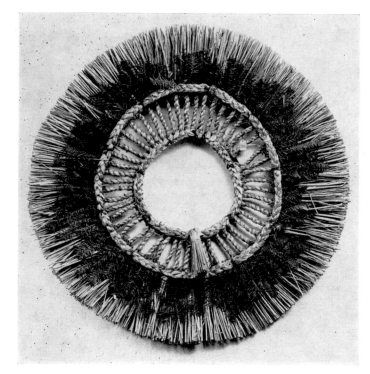

200 *The pine bush outside this inn at Rust on the Neusiedler See, Burgenland, indicates that the inn-keeper sells his own growths there.*

201 *The golden pot in this sign at the pub "Zum Löwen", at Oberjoch in West Germany, promises a good brew.*

and after fermentation selling the wine as such; by putting fragrant herbs into the must or wine and passing it off as muscatel; by adding sugar, sultanas, syrup and a measure of Spanish, Italian or Hungarian wine to home-grown wines, and selling them as imports from these countries; by adulterating the products of their own cellar with sulphur, brandy, and Spanish wines and palming them off as strong southern wines; by falsifying the drink with fruit juices; and finally by using smaller measures than those prescribed in the region.

Only the wine legislation of the last hundred years has brought law and order here. Its net is fine, and its punishments vigorous – much to the benefit of the consumer. But even in the Middle Ages they were strict. In Nuremberg if they caught such adulterators with their wares, then

> "They took them to the slaughterhouse
> Knocked the barrel's bottom out
> And let it in the Pegnitz swim,"

as mastersinger Kunz Hass reported from first hand experience in his 1490 encomium of his native town. The authorities of some towns on the Rhine dealt even more rigorously with particularly severe offenders. After staving in the transgressing barrels before his eyes, they put the trickster in a cage on the end of a draw-well arm, in which he was repeatedly ducked over his head in the Rhine. After such an experience many of them must have lost their taste for wine for a while.

In honour of the wine merchants' guilds it must be said that they did everything in their power to prevent deceptions. Every growth and every blend was subjected to stiff controls. So they are today, only more so. But the criteria have changed. In our days importance is attached to the exact defining of the type of grape used, to origin, vintage, and distinctions of quality such as *Auslese* or *Spätlese*. This kind of description is relatively recent. Formerly people generally contented themselves with geographical data.

Even then they did not always define the place where the grapes were picked and pressed. A classic example of this were the "Bacharach wines", the name under which, until about 1700, all wines offered for sale in this important German market town were known – even though the majority of them had matured in the cellars of the Palatinate and the Rheingau. Direct shipment by water down the Rhine to the consumers of Cologne, Amsterdam and London was prevented by the rapids of the Bingen Hole. Before this dangerous point the barrels had to be transshipped from boats onto wagons. But many of them went straight by road to the point where the Rhine again became navigable – to Bacharach. And this town gave them their sonorous name. When the dangerous underwater obstacle had been blown up, a part of the town's fame disappeared. Men still make good wine in Bacharach, while at the Bingen Hole stands the legendary "Mäuseturm" as a warning for boatmen.

In contrast to Bacharach, the word Tokay has preserved its old, broad significance. The town of that name on the slopes of the Hegyalja does indeed count much vine country within its fields. But it was and is, above all, a market for the growths of the surrounding villages. The Aszú comes from about thirty communes in the district of Borsod Abaúj, from Mád, Tarczal, Tállya, Tolcsva, Sárospatak and Sátoraljaújhely.

## Vinum faecatum

Let us go down from these heights once more into the vale of tears. There too over thousands of years has trickled a watery stream of wine. But it can bear the name of wine only with reservations. It was the drink of those who planted and tended the vines of others. Cato had two recipes for its production. It could be made out of unripe and inferior grapes, and the drink remained sour, very like vinegar. Hardly more attractive was a brew of fresh and boiled must, with vinegar and water added. "This wine will keep until the summer solstice, and what remains will then become sharp, excellent vinegar," observed the old latifundium proprietor. An economical gentleman! Not that he would have been much praised by his slaves and servants for it. Who knows if they would have much preferred two other varieties known in their day: the *lora*, a sub-wine made from the softened husks of grapes, and the *vinum faecatum*, a fermented mixture of water and yeast. *Lora* has survived to the present as a drink for the servants and workers on wine estates. The process may first have been communicated by monasteries.

## Bottles of All Shapes and Colours

Sub-wine on account of its thinness has only rarely, and then for no length of time, found its way into the half-way house of the bottle. This colourful, transparent container, so familiar to us nowadays, was reserved for those growths that had aged in the barrel to full, clear maturity.

It is in fact not so long since wine took up its glass abode. As long ago as the Roman Empire the bottle was attempting to compete with the small clay amphora, but never met with real success. Some remarkably fine pieces from this time have luckily been preserved (Ill. 208). Neither in the Middle Ages did the glass container appear in its present role. Wine was kept in the barrel until such time as decanted into pottery or metal jugs to be brought to the table and poured into cups. Only in the second half of the eighteenth century did a change begin to manifest itself. This was primarily due to the use of the cork from which Dom Pérignon had already profited. This new kind of stopper was the first effective way of sealing the long-drawn-out necks of the bottles against the air. The wine was able to preserve its flavour for a longer period in the cellar because it oxidized much more slowly. It was just this process that had hitherto so seriously affected its quality.

There was, however, still a long way to go to the relatively uniform bottle shapes we know today. Johann Heinrich Zedler's *Complete Universal Lexicon*, appearing in the eighteenth century, listed "vessels great, medium and small, flat, drawn out, round, pressed, angular, at the bottom little or deeply recessed, of green, black and white glass, bare glass or also with engraving, straw or cane woven and entwined." Such a wealth would send every modern bottle fan into raptures.

But the more strongly the new container established its position, the greater was the drive towards standardization. Ways and means had to be found to stack the bottles in as little space

202 *"Pure, fragrant wine"*, is the heading in the Theatrum Sanitatis. *The picture beneath it shows a well-filled wine cellar.*

*The cellarman is allowing his guest to sample the quality of the stored vintage.* Biblioteca Casanatense, Rome.

*203 Good wine and its bush. From: Olaus Magnus,*
*Historia de gentibus septentrionalibus,*
*Rome 1555.*

as possible. For this reason in Germany the beginning of the nineteenth century saw the start of a trend towards the long-necked flute shape. For a long time men have distinguished between brown bottles for Rhine wines and green ones for the products of the Mosel. In Franconia and part of Baden the flattened round Bocksbeutel was preferred. Characteristic for the wine-growing district of Bordeaux is the cylinder shape with a clearly offset narrow neck. The thickset burgundy bottle, by contrast, has a slope-shouldered transition from body to neck. The chianti bottle with its round-bellied, straw-plaited body would fall over without its stand. Every Tokay growth is readily recognizable by its long-necked container, whose colourlessness is characteristic for many other sweet wines.

## Colourful and Informative Labels

But for the uninitiated such nuances of outer shape mean little. To find out what is inside he chiefly reads the text of the small, bright-coloured label on the bottle's side.

These labels have their own history. Their beginnings go back into Antiquity. Much the earliest known document of this type is the seal imprint on the cover of an Egyptian vessel. It declares its contents to be a vintage from the vineyard "Praised be Horus, Lord of Heaven". This plantation belonged to King Djoser, who founded the Third Dynasty of Pharaohs in about

2650 B.C. Later examples are usually more reticent. They generally name the owner and his "wine-growing inspector", who was also responsible for decanting. The vineyard and vintage almost always went unmentioned. They are also omitted from the cylinder seal with which a row of ancient Babylonian vessels were stamped. Between the Euphrates and the Tigris men at this time set most store by the mark of the proprietor.

The Romans brought a new order into things. They began to mark their amphorae with information about origin and age. The vintages were then dated according to the consuls holding office in that year. The innovation is certainly connected with the fact that in the meantime men had learned how to make wine keep for a certain length of time. But we may refrain from passing judgement on the credibility of an inscription reported by Petronius – *Falernum Opimianum annorum centum* (Opimian Falernum, hundred years old) – as having adorned the celebrated glass amphorae at the feast given by Trimalchio. In this juicy and ironical tale the witty satirist allows his nouveau-riche snob a very high flight indeed. But perhaps he only wanted to show how easy it was to hoodwink people, when it came to demonstrating their knowledge of wine. Probably the only truth in the whole tale is that the term of Consul L. Opimius Nepos – 121 B.C. – brought one of the best vintages in the history of the Roman Republic.

The positive aspects of the Roman example found no imitators in the years that followed. Only at the beginning of the nineteenth century, as quality wine-growing began to gain ground and the biggest cellars discovered the advantages of glass bottles, did the forerunners of our modern labels appear. The form and text were at first modest. In essence the informative label was considered a mark of distinction, and only the most noble growths aspired to one. For this reason these "letter wines" as they were known around Cologne, were particularly prized by connoisseurs. Unfortunately much of what came later was to be regretted. It is true that Trimalchio's example was not repeated. Legislators were increasingly insistent that the contents of the bottle should be declared with the necessary clarity. But the label itself became increasingly the arena for all kinds of average to inferior graphic exercises. Even today one cannot look at a fair number of these bright little posters without a slight shudder, and the silent hope that the contents described will outdo them for aesthetic quality. It is regrettable that the modest but perfectly elegant labels from the first half of the nineteenth century inspired so little imitation. People forgot that a good wine also deserves exterior dignity, especially if it is one of the great vintages.

## Great Wines, Wise Drinkers

The chronicle of these outstanding growths stretches back for varying lengths of time in the different wine-growing regions. We have only sparse information on the great vintages of Antiquity. The "Opimian" vintage is known to us through the boasting of Trimalchio. Pliny has it from old informants that the year brought "cooking weather" ("ea coeli temperies fulsit, quam cocturam vocant, solis opere" – through the work of the sun the heavens came into that condition which men call cooking). The expression is still familiar to wine-growers today. The weather in the year 91 must have been similar, for it made the vines flourish and the corn wither. The event is thought to have given Emperor Domitian the final impulse for announcing his legislation aimed at cutting back the cultivation of the vine.

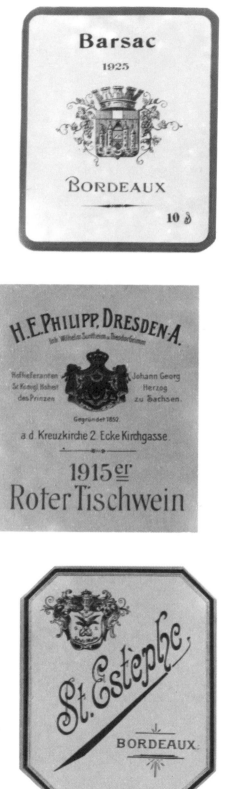

204 *A small selection from the inestimable wealth of wine labels. Wine Collection Rauner, Radebeul near Dresden.*

205 *Chinese inn sign. Museum für Völkerkunde, Leipzig.*

In 1907 Friedrich von Bassermann-Jordan compiled a wine chronicle for southern and south-western Germany which for thoroughness has yet to be matched. His list extends from the fourth to the beginning of the twentieth century. Only some of the great vintages are mentioned here: 742 (hot and dry, very good wine); 990 (hot summer, excellent wine); 1069 (abundant harvest); 1138 (much wine; fertile year); 1194 (hot summer, drought and hailstorms, but excellent harvest); 1259 (a year rich in cereals and wine); 1300 (plenty of wine; the old was offered free to get empty barrels); 1328 (plenty of excellent wine; flowering in April, vintage at the turn of July to August); 1386 (plenty of good wine; shortage of barrels. An empty *Fuderfass* – 1,000 litres – cost four times as much as its contents); 1425 (wine very good, but rotted on the vine, as due to the plague there were no vintagers to be got); 1426 (good, very cheap wine: to drink a heller away you had to go twice to the inn); 1484 (excellent, delicious wine: in Strasbourg they gave fifty litres for an egg); 1540 (so great a heat in Summer that the earth cracked, and in places men could ford the Rhine on horseback. Flowering on the 5th April, beginning of vintage before the end of August, excellent wine); 1631 (hot summer, much fruit and wine; due to barrel shortage much wine kept in tubs); 1699 (a great vintage year on the Rhine); 1718 (terrible heat, nine months of drought; vintage in September – the Gutedel was ripe by the end of July – much very good wine); 1783 (one of the best wine years of all time, very prevalent noble rot; in the Palatinate a 1,200 litre barrel of this vintage brought up to 2,200 guilders); 1811 (fruit almost matched that of 1783 for quality); 1893 (not plentiful, but outstanding in quality). In our century Bacchus has so far sent outstanding vintages in 1911 (known to history after Halley's comet as *Kometenwein*), 1921, 1945, 1947, 1949, 1959.

But looking at this chain of golden years we should not forget that such peaks alternated with at least as many troughs. To show how destructive they could be a few examples will suffice. During the iron Winter and early Spring of 1219 all the vines in Franconia froze. In midsummer of 1338 all ripening fruit was visited by a biblical plague: enormous locust swarms coming from Hungary ate, among other things, the vineyards bare. The remains were destroyed by a premature Winter arriving with much snow at the end of October. About three hundred years later it must have come even earlier. For in 1628 the grapes froze before they were ripe, together with the stocks. "Even vinegar was spoiled with their juice," reported a contemporary. In the Rheingau not a grape was picked.

Let that suffice. We could continue this dark chronicle up to 1956, when about a hundred hectares on the Elbe produced hardly a thousand litres of wine. And yet it seems almost symbolic that the following vintage brought, if not an abundant, at least an excellent quality vintage; and 1958 produced a vintage to burst all barrels at the seams. Thus the growers were given fresh comfort.

The hopes of the sturdy drinker went with them always. If one year was bad, and the vintage small and sour, then perhaps the next vintage would bring abundant compensation. Then throats were opened wide again – if not too wide. With disbelief and shudders we can read of the quantities that formerly flowed down seemingly inexhaustible gullets. In 1351, when the High Master of the Teutonic Order, Winrich von Kniprode, was inaugurated into his office, every guest at the following banquet was obliged to down a silver bowl holding eight tankards full, in one go. Veit von Bassenheim managed this not once but three times, and in reward received for such "knightly" ability the title of a castle captain. We wonder how often he may have stood rather unsteadily upon the battlements of his castle!

With such immoderation the pleasures of wine were lost, whose conditions Socrates some 2,500 years ago expressed in a fine comparison: "With drinking, Sirs, I am completely in agreement, for wine in truth refreshes the soul and lulls the sorrows, as mandrake does man, and awakes instead merriment, as oil does a flame. However, I feel that drinking to men is like the earth to plants. For even they cannot hold themselves upright if the heavens water them too heavily at one time; but if they receive just so much to drink as does them good, then they will not only grow upright, but flourish and be fruitful. And so it shall also be with us."

There is surely no better word to be taken to heart by all those who feel themselves attached in spirit to the pleasures of wine. And if they would follow the wisest of all Athenians in one thing more, let them, where the Ancients began their banquets with a sacrifice of the juice of the vine to their gods, drink with a thought for the health of those who created the conditions for such enjoyment through their labour.

In its way this book, too, is intended as a small contribution of thanks.

206 *Ancient drinking bout. Greek vase painting.*
*Museo Archeologico Nazionale, Naples.*

207 *Servant with wine jug. Etruscan fresco from
the "Grave of the Leopards", 450 B.C.,
Tarquinia.*

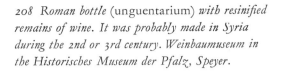

208 Roman bottle (unguentarium) *with resinified remains of wine. It was probably made in Syria during the 2nd or 3rd century. Weinbaumuseum in the Historisches Museum der Pfalz, Speyer.*

209 *This glass bottle demonstrates a design from the end of the 17th century. It held "foundation-stone wine". It is dated 1687 and was found during the demolition of a house at Grossjena on the Unstrut, near Naumburg.*
*Weinbaumuseum in the Historisches Museum der Pfalz, Speyer.*

211

210 *The poet Hafis playing the lute and drinking wine.*
*Persian miniature from* c. *1700. Museum des Kunsthandwerks, Leipzig.*

211 *In Georgia even today at proper drinking bouts one still drinks from horns. Niko Pirosmanashvili in naive epic style captured such a celebration, at about the turn of the century, in a most impressive manner.*

212 *Merry company. Painting by Jan Steen (1626–1679).*
*Mauritshuis Museum, The Hague.*

213 *Harlequin with wine jug. Figure by Johann Joachim Kändler (1706–1775). Porcelain collection of the Staatliche Kunstsammlungen, Dresden.*

214 *With this spoon, made in 1699 and holding about a litre, the merchants of Nuremberg bid their guests welcome. Prälatur-Museum, Seligenstadt.*

215 *From these porcelain cups wine was formerly drunk in Korea. Museum für Völkerkunde, Leipzig.*

216 Colore – Odore – Sapore: the metal sculptor
Fritz Kühn called this composition a sketch in
steel. It characterizes the elements of colour, taste
and aroma that define the quality of a wine. Wine
Collection Rauner, Radebeul near Dresden.

# Sources of Reference

Alanne, Eero: *Die deutsche Weinbauterminologie in althochdeutscher und mittelhochdeutscher Zeit.* Helsinki, 1950.

Andrásfalvy, Bertalan: "Formen des albanischen Weinbaues." In: *Acta Ethnographica* 11, Budapest, 1962, p. 293 ff.

Andrásfalvy, Bertalan: "Der Rotwein in Ungarn." In: *Acta Ethnografica* 14, Budapest, 1965, p. 227 ff.

Andres, Stefan: *Die grossen Weine Deutschlands.* Berlin (West), 1960.

Andrieu, Pierre: *Chronologie anecdotique du Vignoble Français.* Paris (undated).

Andrieu, Pierre: *Petite histoire de l'étiquette.* Paris, 1945.

Arnaldus de Villa Nova: *De vinis.* Strasbourg, 1484.

Arnaudov, M.: *Studii vărchu bălgarskite obredi i legendi*, Parts I/II. Sofia, 1972.

Babo, A. von and E. Mach: *Handbuch des Weinbaues.* Berlin, [4]1924.

Baccius, Andreas: *De naturali vinorum historia ...* Rome, 1596.

Bakó, Ferenc: *Egri borospinék.* Eger, 1961.

Barzen, Robert Michael: "Das Winzermesser und andere Schneidgeräte im römischen Weinbau." In: *Trierisches Jahrbuch 1956*, p. 85 ff.

Bassermann-Jordan, Friedrich von: *Geschichte des Weinbaus*, Vols. I–III. Frankfurt/Main, [2]1923.

Bassermann-Jordan, Friedrich von: *Der Weinbau der Pfalz im Altertum.* Speyer, 1946.

Bauer-Samer, Martha: *Der Weinbau des Nord-Burgenlandes in volkskundlicher Betrachtung.* Eisenstadt, 1954.

Bertsch, Karl and Franz Bertsch: *Geschichte unserer Kulturpflanzen.* Stuttgart, 1949.

Bidet ct Hamel du Monceau: *Traité sur la nature et la culture de la vigne.* Paris, 1753.

Billard, Raymond: *La Vigne dans l'antiquité.* Lyons, 1913.

Bronner, J. Ph: *Der Weinbau in Süddeutschland.* Heidelberg, 1833–1842.

Cardilhac, Paul-Emile: *A l'enseigne de Bacchus.* Paris, 1953.

Carlowitz, Georg Heinrich von: *Versuch einer Culturgeschichte des Weinbaus, von der Urzeit bis auf unsere Zeiten ...* Leipzig, 1846.

Cato, Marcus Porcius: *De agri cultura.* Berlin, 1963.

Christoffel, Karl: *Durch die Zeiten strömt der Wein.* Hamburg, 1957.

Christoffel, Karl: *Wein-Lese-Buch.* Munich, 1964.

Columella, Lucius Iunius Moderatus: *Antike Landwirtschaft.* Translation by Karl Ahrens. Berlin, 1972.

Crescentiis, Petrus de: *Ruralium commodorum libri XII.* Strasbourg, 1486.

Crescentiis, Petrus de: *Opus ruralium commodorum libri XII.* Speyer, 1493.

Crescentiis, Petrus de: *De omnibus agriculturae libri XII.* Basle, 1548.

Daehne, Paul: *Der Holzbauch.* Berlin/Leipzig, 1930.

*Das österreichische Weinbuch*. Vienna (undated).

Debigue, Gérard: *Dictionnaire des vins.* Paris, 1969.

Dehn-Rothfelser, von: *Ein schön Weinbaw-Buch/ Wie man die Weinberge erbauwen soll* ... Leipzig, 1629.

Demnan, J.L.: *The vine and its fruit in relation of production of wine.* London, 1864.

Diriet, H.: *Reben und Wein.* Zurich, 1945.

Dumay, Raymond: *Französische Weine.* Munich, 1969.

Eder, Robert: "Der Bock als Entdecker der Weintraube, der Weinbeerbock und die Weinberggoas." In: *Zeitschrift für österreichische Volkskunde*, Vol. 15, Vienna, 1909, p. 180ff; Vol. 17, 1911, p. 80ff.

Eisler, Robert: *Orphisch-dionysische Mysteriengedanken in der christlichen Antike.* Leipzig, 1925.

Fischer, Heinrich August (H.A.F.): *Oeconomische Abhandlung von gründlich bessern und einträglichern Weinbergsbau.* Dresden/Leipzig, 1765.

Fojtik, Karl: "K dějinám vinařstvi na Moravě." In: *Česky lid* 43, Prague 1956, p. 150ff.

Forbes, R.J.: "Food and Drink." In: Charles Singer and others, *A History of Technology*, Vol. II, Oxford, [4]1967, p. 103ff.; Vol. III, Oxford, [2]1964, p. 1ff.

Frings, Theodor, *Germania Romana*, Vols. I/II. Halle, 1966, 1968.

Frolec, Václav: *Vinohradnické stavby na Slovácku.* Uherské hradiště, 1966.

Frolec, Václav: "Das Rebmesser in den tschechischen Ländern." In: *Vznik a počátky Slovanů.* Prague, 1972, p. 243ff.

Gabalho, Fernando: "Mais alguas notas sobre ferramenta agricola." In: *Trabalhos de Antropologia e Etnologia*, Vol. 18, No. 1/2, Porto, 1960, p. 152ff.

Gatterer, Christoph Wilhelm Jacob: *Litteratur des Weinbaus aller Nationen.* Heidelberg, 1832.

Gollmick, Friedrich and others: *Das Weinbuch.* Leipzig, [2]1970.

Grünn, Helene: *Faßbinder, Faßboden. Handwerk und Kunst.* Vienna/Munich, 1968.

Gutkind, C.S. and K.Wolfskehl: *Das Buch vom Wein.* Munich, 1927.

Hagenow, J.: "Color – Odor – Sapor. Zur Geschichte der Weinbeurteilung und der Weinkultur." In: *Deutsches Weinbau-Jahrbuch* 20, Waldkirchen i.Br., 1969, p. 195ff.

Halász, Zoltán: *Das Buch vom Ungarwein.* Budapest, 1958.

Hartmeyer, Hans: *Der Weinhandel im Gebiete der Hanse im Mittelalter.* Leipzig, 1904.

Hegi, Gustav (in collaboration with H.Beger): *Rebstock und Wein.* Munich, 1925.

Hehn, Victor: *Kulturpflanzen und Haustiere in ihrem Übergang aus Asien nach Griechenland und Italien sowie in das übrige Europa.* Hildesheim, [9]1963.

Heller, Paul: "Der Weinbau in Glaube und Aberglaube." In: *Deutsches Weinbau-Jahrbuch* 17, Waldkirchen i.Br., 1966, p. 166ff.

Henderson, Alexander: *The history of ancient and modern wines.* London, 1824.

Herodot: *Das Geschichtswerk des Herodotos von Halikarnassos.* Leipzig, 1956.

Heyne, Moriz: *Das deutsche Nahrungswesen von den ältesten geschichtlichen Zeiten bis zum 16. Jahrhundert.* Leipzig, 1901.

Hilpert, Marianne: *Von Häckern und Winzern am Maindreieck.* Würzburg, 1957.

Horn, M. Georg: *Hierampelos. Das ist Bericht vom Weinbaw* ... Schmalkalden, 1585.

Hubschmid, Johannes: *Schläuche und Fässer.* Berne, 1955.

Johnson, Hugh: *Der große Weinatlas.* Berne/Stuttgart, 1972.

Johnson, Hugh and Arne Krüger: *Das große Buch vom Wein.* Munich, 1969.

Jung, Hermann: *Wein in der Kunst.* Munich, 1961.

Jung, Hermann: *Traubenmadonnen und Wein-heilige*. Duisburg, 1964.

Jung, Hermann: *Visitenkarten des Weins*. Duisburg, 1966.

Kahounova, Ema: *L'udové vinobradnické stavby a lisy*. Bratislava, 1969.

Kressmann, Edouard: *Der Französische Wein-führer*. Munich, 1971.

Kutter, Wilhelm: "Der Wein im Brauch." In: *Das Buch vom deutschen Wein*. Mainz, 1954/55, p. 35 ff.

Ladurner-Parthanes, Matthias: *Vom Perglwerk zum Torggl*. Bozen, 1972.

Lagrange, André: *Moi, je suis vigneron*. Ville-franche-en-Beaujolais, 1960.

Lagrange, André: "Musée de vin de Bourgogne à Beaune. Catalogue." In: *Arts et Traditions Populaires* 13, Paris, 1965, No. 2.

Lauenstein, Werner: *Das mittelalterliche Böttcher- und Küferhandwerk in Deutschland mit besonderer Rücksicht auf Lübeck, Köln, Frankfurt/Main, Basel und Überlingen*. Berlin, 1917.

Lekiašvili, A.: *V strane vinogradnoj loz y. Očerki iz istorii vinogradstvo v Gruzii*. Tbilissi, 1972. *Lexique de la Vigne et du Vin*. Paris, 1963.

Lobé, Joseph and others: *Le Grand Livre du Vin*. Lausanne, 1969.

Loeschke, Siegfried: *Denkmäler vom Weinbau aus der Zeit der Römerherrschaft an Mosel, Saar und Ruwer*. Trier, 1933.

Lühmann, Werner: *St. Urban*. Würzburg, 1968.

Lukas, Jan: *Das Buch vom Wein*. Prague, 1964.

Maurizio, A.: *Geschichte der gegorenen Getränke*. Wiesbaden, ²1970.

Meyer, Hans Moritz: "Wein-Bibliographie." In: *Der deutsche Weinbau* (since 1954 *Die Weinwissenschaft*), Mainz, 1953 ff.

Michajlov, G.: *Trakite*. Sofia, 1972.

Mironescu, N. A. and Paul Petrescu: "Construcţiile viticole din zona Huşilor." In: *Revista de Folclor* 8, Bucharest, 1963, p. 140 ff.

Mone, F. J.: "Beiträge zur Weingeschichte." In: *Zeitschrift für die Geschichte des Oberrheins*, Vol. 14, Karlsruhe, 1862, p. 29 ff.

Müller, Karl: *Weinbau-Lexikon*. Berlin, 1930.

Nestle, Karl Theodor and Paul Emer: *Geschichte der Weinflasche*. Mönchengladbach, 1964.

Nilsson, M. P.: *Griechische Feste von religiöser Bedeutung*. Leipzig, 1906.

Nordhoff, J. B.: *Der vormalige Weinbau in Norddeutschland*. Münster, ²1883.

Oppermann, D. J.: *Spirit of the Vine*. Cape Town, 1968.

Orizet, Louis: *Vinboken*. Stockholm (undated).

Otto, Walter F.: *Dionysos, Mythos und Kultur*. Frankfurt/Main, ²1939.

Pacottet, Paul: *Viticulture*. Paris, 1905.

Palladius, R. Taurus Aemilianus: *Opus Agriculturae*. Leipzig, 1898.

Parain, Charles: "Vorindustrielle Pressen und Keltern und ihre Verbreitung in Westeuropa." In: *Deutsches Jahrbuch für Volkskunde*, Vol. 8, Berlin, 1962, p. 338 ff.

Parain, Charles: "Voies et formes de la différenciation dans les vignobles du nord-est de la France: Champagne et Lorraine." In: *Arts et Traditions Populaires* 16, Paris 1968, Nos. 3–4, p. 201 ff.

Pastor, Eilert: *Deutsche Volksweisheit in Wetterregeln und Bauernsprüchen*. Berlin, 1934.

Peneva-Săbeva, Lilija: "Tradicionno lozarstvo i vinarstvo v Petričko i Melniško." In: *Izvestija na Etnografskija Institut i Musej*, 13, Sofia, 1971, p. 53 ff.

Pieper, Richard: *Volksbotanik*. Gumbinnen, 1897.

Plinius, Secundus Gaius: *Naturalis historiae*, Vols. 1–5, Leipzig, 1870–1897.

Puvis, A.: *De la culture de la vigne et de la fabrication du vin chez les anciens*. Paris, 1847.

Reichelt, Karl: *Beiträge zur Geschichte des ältesten Weinbaus in Deutschland und dessen Nachbarländern bis zum Jahre 1000 n.Chr.* Reutlingen, 1886.

217 *Grapes on a Moravian faience jug, 1810. Moravské Museum, Brno.*

Remark, Peter: *Der Weinbau im Römerreiche.* Munich, 1927.

Rohr, Julius Bernhard von: *Viticultura Germaniae Oeconomica …* Leipzig, 1730.

Roller, Otto: "Die Baumkelter im Weinmuseum des Historischen Museums der Pfalz." In: *Mitteilungen des Historischen Vereins der Pfalz*, Vol. 67, Speyer, 1969, p. 347 ff.

Rubens, Johann Ferdinand: *Winzerbuch.* Hanover/Leipzig, ²1875.

Schams, Franz: *Ungarns Weinbau*, Vol. I/II. Pesth, 1832.

Scheuermeier, Paul: *Bauernwerk in Italien, der italienischen und spätromanischen Schweiz*, Vol. I/II. Zurich, 1943; Berne, 1956.

Schmidt, Leopold: "Die Rebmesser unserer alten Weinhauer." In: *Bauernbundkalender*, Vienna, 1958, p. 70 ff.

Schoonmaker, Frank: *Das Wein-Lexikon.* Munich, 1967.

Schreiber, Georg: "Zur Symbolik, Sprache und Volkskunde des Weines." In: *Beiträge zur sprachlichen Volksüberlieferung*, Berlin, 1953, p. 208 ff.

Simon, André L.: *Die grossen Weine Frankreichs.* Berlin (West), 1958.

Simon, André L. and others: *Wines of the World.* London/New York/Toronto/Sydney, 1967.

Speck, E.: *Handelsgeschichte des Altertums.* Vol. I ff., Leipzig, 1900 ff.

Steigelmann, Wilhelm: *Der Wein in der Bibel.* Neustadt/Weinstrasse, 1962.

Strabon, Amasinus: *Geographica*, Vols. 1–3. Leipzig, 1904–1915.

Thienemann, Friedrich August Ludwig: *Literatur der Weinwissenschaft in alphabetischer Anordnung.* Dresden, 1839.

Thomas, Alois: *Die Darstellung Christi in der Kelter.* Düsseldorf, 1936.

Thudichum, Georg: *Traube und Wein in der Kulturgeschichte.* Tübingen, 1881.

Troost, Gerhard: *Die Technologie des Weines.* Stuttgart, ³1961.

Varro, Marcus Terentius: *De re rustica*, Vols. 1–3. Leipzig, ²1929.

Veith, Werner: *Die schlesische Weinbauterminologie.* Marburg, 1966.

Vincze, István: "Verfahren und Geräte der Weinkelterung unter besonderer Berücksichtigung des Weingebietes von Nordostungarn." In: *Acta Ethnographica*, Vol. 10, Budapest, 1961, p. 295 ff.

Vincze, István: "Historische Schichten und Kultureinflüsse in der ungarischen Weinkultur. (Zur Frage der ethnographischen Systematisierung der ungarischen Weinkultur.)" In: *Europa et Hungaria*, Budapest, 1965, p. 173 ff.

Vispre, F.: *A dissertation on the growth of Vine in England.* London, 1786.

Vogt, Ernst (Editor): *Weinbau.* Stuttgart, ³1960.

Wartburg, Walter von: "Die griechische Kolonisation in Südgallien und ihre sprachlichen Zeugen im Westromanischen." In: von Wartburg, *Von Sprache und Mensch*, Berne, 1956, p. 61 ff.

Weber, Heinrich: *Bamberger Weinbuch.* Bamberg, 1884.

Weinhold, Rudolf: "Rebmesser und Kelter." In: *Deutsches Jahrbuch für Volkskunde*, Vol. 12, Berlin, 1966, p. 37 ff.

Weinhold, Rudolf: *Winzerarbeit an Elbe, Saale und Unstrut.* Berlin, 1973.

Weise, Paul: *Beiträge zur Geschichte des römischen Weinbaus in Gallien und an der Mosel.* Hamburg, 1901.

Weiss-Bass, E. Friedrich: *Weingewerbe und Weinleutenzunft im alten Basel.* Basle, 1958.

Woschek, Heinz Gert: *Der Wein.* Munich, 1971.

Younger, William: *Gods, Men and Wine.* London, 1966.

"Zemedelski zakon. Lex agraria." In: *Izvori za bălgarskata istorija*, Part VI. Sofia, 1960, p. 208 ff.

Zitzen, E. G.: *Der Wein in der Wort- und Wirtschaftsgeschichte.* Bonn, 1952.

# Sources of Illustrations

*218 A secret tasting. Miniature for an initial A from the* Livre de Santé *of Aldebrandin de Sienne, 14th century.*

The photos reproduced in this book were kindly supplied by:

Akademie der Wissenschaften der DDR/ Zentralinstitut für Geschichte, Dresden 1, 2, 3, 4, 31, 32, 58, 71, 114, 128, 129, 130, 175

Art Centrum, Prague 57, 88, 107, 150, 185

Aufsberg, Lala, Sonthofen/Allgäu 15, 18, 19, 28, 40, 41, 42, 47, 61, 67, 69, 77, 86, 89, 96, 105, 149, 188, 197, 198, 200, 201, 214

Bayerisches Hauptstaatsarchiv, Munich 56

Bayerisches Nationalmuseum, Munich 26

Bibliothèque Nationale, Paris 84, 140

British Museum, London 13, 24, 25, 43, 44, 63, 101, 142

F. Bruckmann KG Bildarchiv, Munich 17, 23

Deutsche Fotothek Dresden 29, 39, 78, 83, 93, 109, 120, 123, 126, 141, 190, 211, 213, 216

Fasching, Herbert, Wilhelmsburg/Austria 102, 199

Foto-Ritter, Vienna 37

Foto-Toso, Venice 122

France, Frankfurt/Main 91, 118, 119, 165, 189

Giraudon, Paris 27, 46, 97, 100, 196

Graphische Sammlung der Zentralbibliothek Zurich 34

Hauptamt für Hochbauwesen, Nuremberg 36, 95

Hirmer-Fotoarchiv, Munich 21, 143

Jordanova, Elvina, Sofia 113, 115

Lauros/Giraudon, Paris 6, 48

Dr. R. Maag Ltd., Dielsdorf-Zurich 65, 66, 87

Martin-von-Wagner-Museum der Universität Würzburg 111, 112

Matt, Leonhard von, Buochs/Switzerland 8, 9, 11, 12, 16, 62, 64, 99, 103, 124, 139, 169, 172, 207

MTI, Budapest 73, 74, 94, 167, 184

Musée d'Art et d'Histoire, Geneva 55

Museum des Kunsthandwerks, Leipzig 210

Museum für Völkerkunde, Leipzig 22, 205, 215

Nowosti, Berlin 121, 144, 145, 162, 166, 186, 192, 193, 194

Popperfoto, London 49, 52, 72, 79, 90, 154, 156, 164, 179

Rheinisches Bildarchiv, Cologne 60

Scala, Florence 7, 10, 14, 20, 45, 68, 85, 98, 116, 117, 127, 147, 170, 195, 206, 212 and front of dust-jacket

Staatliche Kunstsammlungen Dresden 38, 125, 177

Staatliche Museen Preussischer Kulturbesitz, Gemäldegalerie, Berlin (West) 80

Staněk, Ol., Brno 81, 82, 217, 219

Süddeutscher Verlag, Munich 104

Universitätsbibliothek Leipzig/Pinkert 5, 30, 33, 35, 59, 70, 108, 131, 132, 157, 158, 161, 176, 203

V-Dia-Verlag, Heidelberg 110

Vivarelli/Gulla, Rome 159, 160, 202

Wacker-Chemie GmbH, Archive 133

Weinbaumuseum im Historischen Museum der Pfalz, Speyer 171, 173, 174, 178, 180, 181, 182, 183, 187, 208, 209

Wine Institute, San Francisco 53, 54, 106, 146, 168

ZEFA, Düsseldorf 50, 51, 75, 76, 92, 148, 151, 152, 153, 155, 163, 191

# *Index*

*219 Moravian faience plate, 1759. In the centre grapes, pruning knife and mattock. Moravské Museum, Brno.*